D1327992

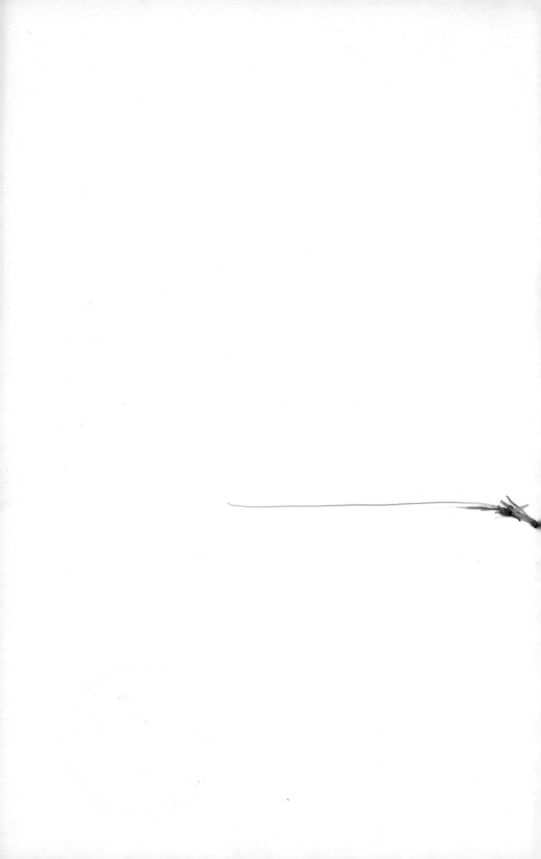

THE
LOGARITHMIC
CENTURY

by

RALPH E. LAPP

PRENTICE-HALL, INC.
Englewood Cliffs, N.J.

The Logarithmic Century by Ralph E. Lapp
Copyright © 1973 by Ralph E. Lapp

Printed in the United States of America

Prentice-Hall International, Inc., London
Prentice-Hall of Australia, Pty. Ltd., North Sydney
Prentice-Hall of Canada, Ltd., Toronto
Prentice-Hall of India Private Ltd., New Delhi
Prentice-Hall of Japan, Inc., Tokyo

10   9   8   7   6   5   4   3   2   1

Library of Congress Cataloging in Publication Data
Lapp, Ralph Eugene.
    The logarithmic century.

    1.   United States—Economic conditions—1971-
2.   Consumption (Economics)—United States.
3.   Economic development.   4.   Technology—Social
aspects.   I.   Title.
HC106.6.L36   330.9'73'092   72-13545
ISBN 0-13-539114-3

CONTENTS

1 America's Growth—End in Sight? 1

2 Hell on Wheels 23

3 The Great Burnup 57

4 The Growth of Nuclear Power 83

5 The Consumer Avalanche 107

6 The Knowledge Explosion 135

7 The Question of Growth 161

8 The Control of Technology 195

9 The Affluent Island 213

Index 255

All progress is based upon a universal innate desire on the part of every organism to live beyond its means.

Samuel Butler

THE
LOGARITHMIC
CENTURY

CHAPTER

1

AMERICA'S GROWTH—END IN SIGHT?

An obsession with growth—growth in populations, in the number and variety of things, in the volume of all things consumable—has formed a conspicuous thread in the texture of twentieth-century civilization. When Cardinal Newman wrote in 1864, "Growth is the only evidence of life," he articulated a credo so widely and fervently held that before another century had passed, the world was suffocating in a surfeit of things and had been infected by a veritable contagion of people.

The growth of an individual organism is halted by natural limitations. From an initial twinning of cells, an organism swiftly doubles in weight, then doubles again, and again. But the intervals between doublings lengthen, and in mammals the growth rate diminishes to a fraction long before the individual reaches maturity. Up to that point, the vertical growth of a human being can be represented on a graph as an ascending straight line (Fig. 1-1). After maturity, vertical growth normally ceases; the graph "bends over," then continues on a plateau through middle age, and may drop slightly on the right in old age.

Lacking the built-in biological controls of the individual —an intricate set of genetic instructions imprinted in the cells—populations can keep on doubling uninterruptedly, up

1

to the point where the demand for whatever the individuals need for survival exceeds the supply. Human beings need air, water, food, shelter, enough space to move around in, tools, and transportation. Modern Americans are making such excessive and gaudy demands for varieties of some of the last-named items on the list that they are jeopardizing the viability of the essential first four.

The solution to the problems caused by growth is easy: just order it stopped. Easy, that is, if you are God. A mere

FIGURE 1-1

GROWTH OF AN INDIVIDUAL

A graph of the vertical growth of Christopher Lapp, who has been measured every Christmas since his birth, illustrates the fallacies of "straight-line" projections. Christopher's height had more than doubled by his first birthday, but it was not to double again until he was past thirteen. If the straight line up to that point is continued to the edge of the graph, it predicts that he will be 6 feet 8 inches tall before he is twenty. That is possible, but not probable. Pushing the projection along the upper curve leads to circuslike growth in the twenties. Analysis of Christopher's height-weight data for his preteenage growth indicates he is in the 90 percentile group, so I would estimate he will reach about 6 feet 2 inches at maturity—somewhat above the probable curve. Future editions of this book will furnish up-to-date statistics on the accuracy of the prediction.

2

FIGURE 1-1

GROWTH OF AN INDIVIDUAL

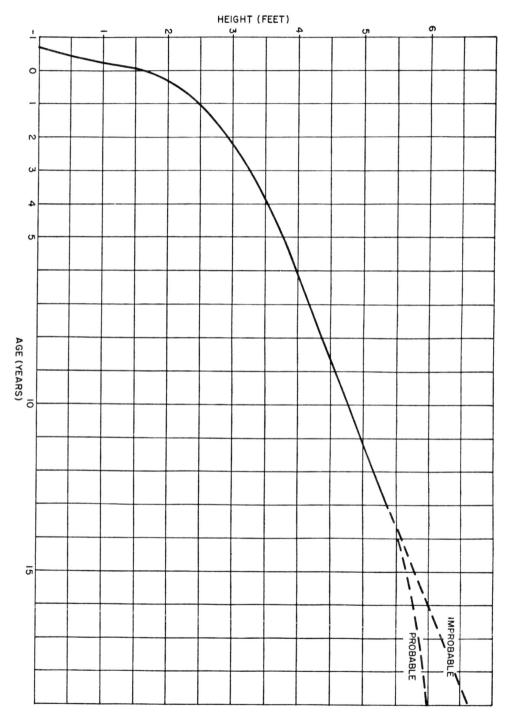

mortal, at least one in a democracy, cannot be so peremptory. To persuade his fellow citizens that changing their historic life-style is imperative, he must equip himself with irrefutable facts. To convince America, the cradle of boosterism, that growth per se does not pave the road to heaven, and may in fact be no more than another good intention, takes more than appeals to altruism. Many Americans are allergic to the word *planning,* since it smacks of government controls and an abridgment of individual rights. But the real answer to

FIGURES 1-2 and 1-3

GROWTH OF A NATION

These two graphs are constructed from the same data, but they differ in method of presentation. Figure 1-2 is a linear plot of the growth of the U.S. population. To squeeze onto a single piece of paper both the statistics of the past and those projected for the future, the first century of growth is compacted into a tiny section of the graph. Figure 1-3 is plotted on semilogarithmic graph paper; this retains the linear scale for the horizontal data but uses a compressed, nonlinear scale for the vertical. On a semilogarithmic graph, the data on early growth can be spread out, and we can see that they form a perfectly straight line. This straight-line relationship between time and population increase can be expressed in an exact mathematical equation. (It is not necessary to understand logarithms to be able to interpret the graphs. [The logarithmic scale is simply a ratio scale, as will be seen by noting that the left-hand scale in Figure 1-3 displays the same vertical distance from 1 to 2 as from 2 to 4 and from 4 to 8 and so forth.] For example, to determine how long it took the population of 10 million to double, draw a line from the 10 million point on the population scale and another from the 20 million point, then measure the distance between the vertical lines where the arrows meet. Each horizontal interval corresponds to 20 years; thus we estimate that the doubling time for the U.S. population before the Civil War was twenty-four years. Semilogarithmic graphs will be used throughout the rest of this book.)

4

FIGURE 1-2

GROWTH OF A NATION

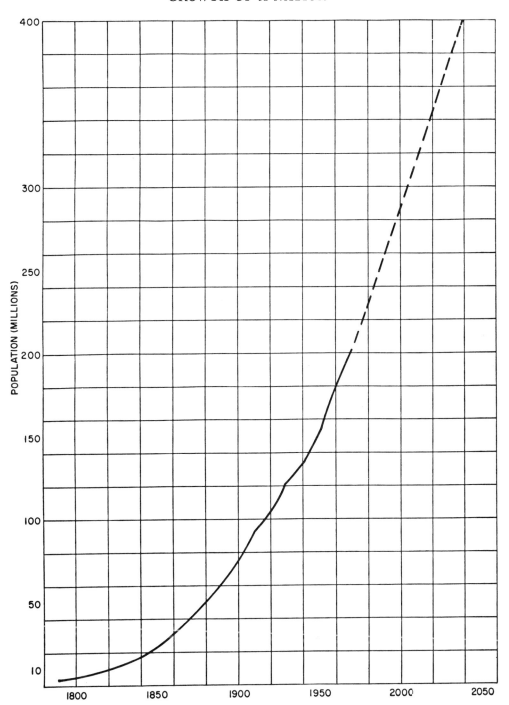

FIGURE 1-3

GROWTH OF A NATION

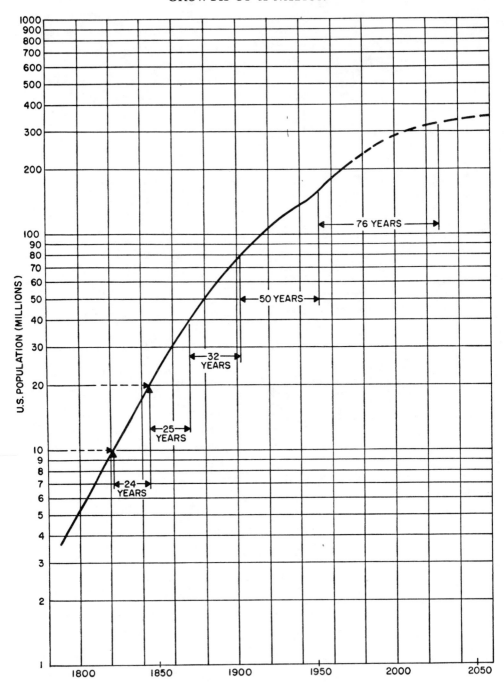

runaway growth is to look ahead, to assess the consequences, and to plan for an orderly future. In looking ahead, we shall bank on the instrument of graphical or statistical presentations, using the past as prologue. It is therefore useful to examine some practical concepts for the description of growth.

The concept of doubling time is very useful in considering growth. We can estimate from Figure 1-2, for example, that before the Civil War, the U.S. population doubled every twenty-four years, or at a rate of slightly less than 3 percent per year. Your bank account does not increase fast enough at that rate of interest, but if the U.S. population had continued to grow at that rate, it would have reached 100 million by 1900. In reality, the doubling time had increased to thirty-two years before the turn of the century, then it lengthened to fifty years. Crystal balls are made from the same imperfect material now as in the past, but I optimistically assume that the next doubling will not occur for a century; that is, the population will not reach the 400 million mark before the 2070s, or a generation beyond the date that would be indicated by continuing the straight line in Figure 1-3. That forecast assumes some degree of population control. The United States now makes such a high per capita demand on its resources, and contaminates the environment so grossly in satisfying that demand, that limiting the population growth is a rational course to take.

A society, like the smallest organism, needs energy in order to grow. Indeed, in the cellular scheme of things the very size of a cell is determined by energy transport mechanisms, and although an elephant may be a hundred thousand fold larger than a mouse, its cells are not very much larger. Human populations have not as yet realized the significance of energy limitations, but awareness of finite fuel resources is just beginning to have an impact on man.

Let us look, for example, at the growth of electric-energy consumption in this country (Figure 1-4). In the early part of the century, the boom was chiefly due to the increase in the use of electricity by industry and by the cities as they replaced horse-drawn public conveyances with trolley cars, and gas lamps with electric lights. The rate of increase (about 12 percent per year) was maintained as the public began to demand residential wiring. There was little doubt that America was hooked on the kilowatt. After a dip during the Depression, the rate of increase resumed its steady climb and has maintained it to the present.

Within this quarter-century, however, I expect the rate of increase to taper off. The slight bending over (lower dotted line in Fig. 1-4) may not seem to make much difference,

FIGURE 1-4

U.S. ELECTRIC ENERGY PRODUCTION
(1900–2000)

The per capita consumption of kilowatt-hours (the unit of energy used by utilities to bill customers) was small in 1900 when few homes were wired for electricity. A kilowatt is a measure of power, i.e., it equals power capable of lighting ten 100-watt electric bulbs. Burning these bulbs for one hour uses one kilowatt-hour of electric energy. The big users in 1900 were industry and the cities. After the cities had replaced horse-drawn public vehicles with streetcars and gas lamps with electric lights, the new form of power caught on and public demand soared, doubling in as little as six years, or at a yearly growth of about 12 percent. From the mid-thirties to the present, the increase shows up as a straight line. If the rate of increase is continued into the future (upper dotted line), it indicates a consumption of 30 trillion kilowatt-hours in the year 2020. For an assumed population of 300 million, that would be a per capita demand of 100,000 kilowatt-hours a year— about twelve times as much as is used at present. For reasons explained in the text, the author regards the lower dotted line as a more realistic projection of future use.

FIGURE 1-4

U.S. ELECTRIC ENERGY PRODUCTION
(1900–2000)

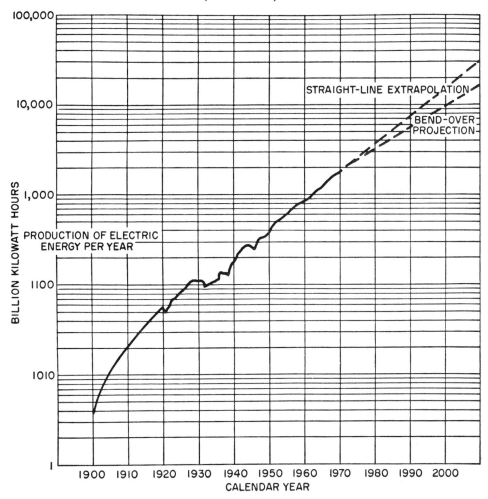

but if it extends into the twenty-first century, it will radically change the electric-energy picture. Even that sanguine projection will disappoint the environmentalists who advocate an immediate and permanent cutback in the production of electric energy. They will be unhappier still to learn that most of whatever increase there is in demand for kilowatt-hours will be supplied by nuclear generators. But the facts about our present resources and reserves make that conclusion inescapable.

A more revered index to economic growth than the consumption of electric energy is the *gross national product*

FIGURE 1-5

THE GROSS NATIONAL PRODUCT (1900–1970)

During the first thirty years of the century, the GNP (gross dollar value of all goods and services produced annually in the U.S.) increased at an average rate of more than 6 percent a year, then capsized into the trough of the Great Depression. Climbing out of that, it escalated rapidly until the mid-century, stimulated by a wartime boom that doubled it every seven or eight years. Since mid-century, the curve has returned to a 6 percent annual growth rate. However, the fact that the dollar is not a constant value, like the kilowatt-hour, but changes from year to year, necessitates an adjustment in the vertical scale to what economists call "constant dollars," usually meaning 1929 dollars for the first half-century and 1958 dollars thereafter. The adjustment to constant dollars would, in effect, shrink the vertical scale, deflating the current dollar and giving a more accurate picture of economic growth. For example, replotting the first thirty years of the century shows that the GNP doubled in the first twenty-five years, or increased at a rate of 3 percent a year, not 6 percent. Replotting the whole chart would indicate that the GNP has risen less than tenfold in constant dollars during the past seven decades, not the sixtyfold the chart represents.

FIGURE 1-5

THE GROSS NATIONAL PRODUCT (1900–1970)

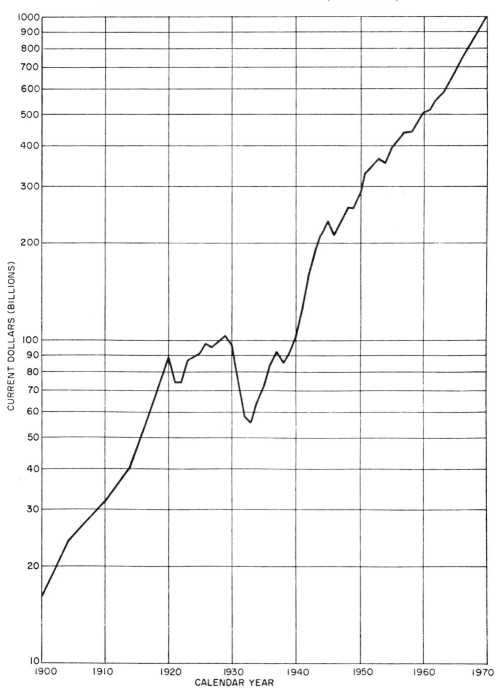

(GNP), which is the term for the gross dollar value of all goods and services produced annually in the country (Fig. 1-5).

Businessmen have made such a fetish of the GNP that they, along with a multitude of less dollar-oriented people, promote growth as almost an end in itself. The data on carloadings of coal were followed carefully as an index of business activity. No one had paid much attention to the deterioration in the quality of life that coal mining and coal burning have brought to some parts of our society. The steelmaker needed coal to fire his furnaces and turn out more steel; the utility executive needed more of it to meet the burgeoning demand for electricity. Each ton of coal had a value, which was added to the total of the gross national product. But where was the national accounting for the thousands of miners with black-lung disease? What about the deterioration of the metropolitan environment as sulfurous fumes descended from coal-burning plants to attack the lungs of millions of city dwellers, even eroding the stone and metals of buildings?

A cynical economist might say: "Oh, we add in the cost of hospital care; and defacing our buildings is good for business—it means we replace them sooner." But this makes a mockery of the GNP as an indicator of national activity. True, it may reflect a barographic record of business output, but it is a tail-chasing economy that pollutes and then reckons in the cost of repairing the damage as one of the signs of economic health.

One is tempted to add another chart to this chapter, plotting the quality of life since 1900. In fact, I have seen some computer-made charts of this type, but I submit that no one knows how to concoct a suitable vertical scale for the quality of life. To appreciate how much industrial progress and our modern way of living have cost us, I suggest that the reader consider Table 1-1, the single table that appears in the 1972 report of the U.S. Council on Environmental Quality.

TABLE 1-1

NATIONWIDE EMISSION OF AIR POLLUTANTS BY WEIGHT (1970)
(in millions of tons per year)

Source	Carbon Monoxide	Particu-lates	Sulfur Oxides	Hydro-carbons	Nitrogen Oxides
Transportation	111.0	0.7	1.0	19.5	11.7
Fuel Combustion (Stationary Sources)	0.8	6.8	26.5	0.6	10.0
Industrial Processes	11.4	13.1	6.0	5.5	0.2
Waste Disposal and Miscellaneous	24.0	4.8	0.4	9.1	0.8
Totals	147.2	25.4	33.9	34.7	22.7

I have not presented the grand total of all these five pollutants because the relative toxicity of carbon monoxide or of any other pollutant is not known. It would be misleading to add all five pollutants together because this assumes they are equally injurious to the environment. Nor do these "big five" constitute the whole of the air-pollution threat. The Environmental Protection Agency (EPA), for example, lists in addition:

Oxidants	Nickel
Fluorides	Manganese
Lead	Zinc
Polycyclic organic matter	Copper
Hydrogen sulfide	Barium
Asbestos	Boron
Beryllium	Mercury

13

Hydrogen chloride	Selenium
Chlorine	Chromium
Arsenic	Pesticides
Cadmium	Radioactive substances
Vanadium	Aeroallergens

EPA estimates: "The annual toll of air pollution on health, vegetation, materials and property values . . . [is] more than $16 billion annually."

This is the assault by the instruments of our economy on our atmosphere alone. But the total impact includes releases to the soil and to water, affecting the biosphere as a whole, the thin earth-water-air shell of the planet providing sustenance to man. Although shopworn by now, the cliché that affluence has been purchased at the price of effluence is still pertinent. And only recently have we even bothered to count the costs—the Council on Environmental Quality was created in 1970 along with EPA. In effect we allowed our economy to roll along with neither a true keeping of accounts nor a national watchdog until seven decades of the century had elapsed.

Today's American has roughly five times the real income of his counterpart seventy years ago, and he enjoys creature comforts unknown or unavailable to the common man then. For example, the 1970 census discloses the degree of U.S. family opulence in terms of household-product ownership. (Since most families live on credit, I substitute the word *possession* for ownership.)

Appliance or Device	Family Possession
Dishwasher	23.7 percent
Air-conditioner	36.7
Color television	37.8
Two or more television sets	29.4
At least one television set	95.0
One automobile	80.0
Two or more automobiles	29.3

14

Washing machine	91.9
Clothes dryer	40.3
Freezer	29.6
Refrigerator	99.8

The architect Le Corbusier wrote, "A house is a machine for living," but I doubt that he had in mind that a house would become an electromechanical menagerie. This mechanization of the American household has been made possible by the electrification of everything from garbage-disposal units to electric toothbrushes. At last count my own household contained twenty electric motors, and I scored 100 percent on possession of the devices listed above. It would be easy for me to agree to zero growth of electric power from this moment forward, but what about the 76 percent of American families who have no dishwasher?

To most Americans electric energy appears to be so clean that they do not associate its production with pollution. Plugging in a vacuum cleaner or a toaster produces heat and power, which is ultimately dissipated as heat, but this in-home cleanliness conceals the basic dirtiness of many utility power plants. Burning a 100-watt bulb for ten hours takes 1 kilowatt-hour of electricity. At the central station, that requires the burning of just under a pound of coal, or its heat equivalent in other fuel. Even further concealed from the average person is the resource consumption and pollution involved in manufacturing the various material things that make up a household. A woman reaches into a kitchen drawer, tears off a sheet of aluminum foil, and never thinks of the electric energy that went into refining the aluminum— several pounds of coal consumed for a package of foil.

If American businessmen have disdained measures to protect the environment in their headlong pursuit of profits, consumers have also been negligent. Take, for example, the consumption of cigarettes in the United States. Admittedly, the U.S. government long neglected to require an admonition on the package, but no one ever claimed that tobacco was good for you.

A century ago cigarette production was limited by the technology of rolling the paper tubes of tobacco; this was a hand operation for which the practiced fingers of French girls were well suited. A trained worker could turn out about four cigarettes a minute, so a pack of twenty took five minutes of labor. In 1883 a Virginia gentleman named James Bonsack devised a mechanical gadget for turning out cigarettes efficiently. Thirteen years later the national production exceeded 1 billion cigarettes per year, and an era of high-pressure advertising began. High taxes, restrictive legislation,

FIGURE 1-6

U.S. CIGARETTE PRODUCTION

The U.S. addiction to cigarette smoking is all too apparent, despite great publicity over the harmful effects of smoking. While a considerable number of people have quit the tobacco habit, over 10 million are heavy smokers, meaning more than one pack per day. The average smoker burns up about 25 pounds of tobacco annually.

FIGURE 1-6

U.S. CIGARETTE PRODUCTION

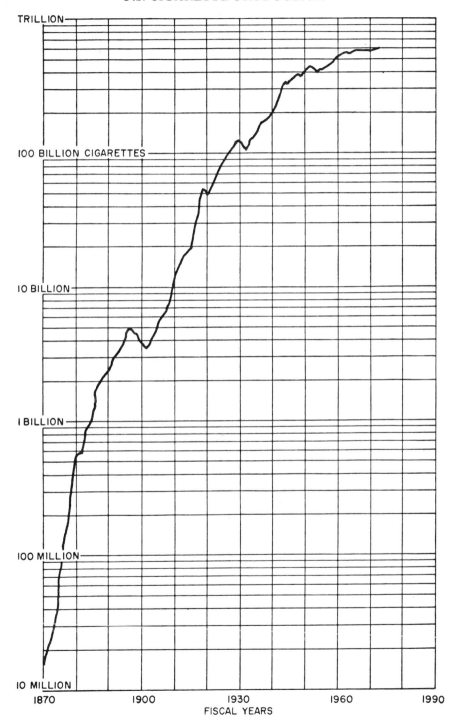

and some nasty rumors that cigarettes caused insanity combined to set sales back at the turn of the century, but then the tobacco industry reorganized and created giant corporations, like the American Tobacco Company. Camels were promoted in 1913 by means of an elaborate national advertising campaign featuring catchy slogans. Sales climbed and topped the 100 billion mark in 1927, peaking after a quarter-century growth at a 14 percent annual rate of increase. Growth then slowed, but at a rate that seemed headed for a trillion-per-year production by 1960. But before then tobacco health hazards were being publicized and sales declined, reaching a plateau of about 570 billion cigarettes per year in the late 1960s.

The growth curve of cigarette sales is typical of initial very rapid increases, followed by slowing, but still growing, sales and then gradual bending over as market saturation is reached. A towel immersed in a basin of water can absorb only so much liquid; we say that it is saturated. In the case of cigarette sales, presumably more sales can be attained through aggressive, if not ruthless or pitiless, advertising and appeal to youth. But when 75 million Americans are puffing away at the rate of one pack a day, the market is rather saturated. Indeed, had it not been for switching to filter tips and mentholated brands and highly deceptive promotion, cigarette sales could have slumped in the past few years.

A factor tending to support the continued high sales of cigarettes is the sheer size and constituency of the tobacco industry. According to the president of the Tobacco Institute, 3 million members of farm families in twenty-two states earn their principal livelihood from raising tobacco, and one hundred thousand workers are gainfully employed in processing it. This is the "tobacco-agricultural-industrial complex." Together, these farm and factory employees account for an annual payroll of close to $2 billion. Federal, state, and local taxes add up to $4.6 billion for all tobacco products, with cigarettes accounting for 98 percent of the revenue. The cigarette industry is an example of a different impact of the economy on the environment. Its significance to farmers and to industrialists is well understood by legislators of the twenty-two tobacco-growing states, but the ultimate impact is on the most intimate environment of all, a person's lungs, where the interface between human tissue and pollutants is measured in human cells.

How does it happen that so many Americans continue to smoke cigarettes when they are warned on every pack that smoking *is* dangerous to human health? I think it is because the smoker cannot see an immediate cause-effect relationship. The fairly subtle message of the surgeon general does not really frighten the smoker into giving up his habit. As Henry L. Mencken wrote in his *Book of Prefaces:* "The public demands certainties: it must be told definitely and a bit raucously that this is true and that is false. But there *are* no certainties." I suspect that this applies to the smoker, especially the one who is habituated to two packs a day. But many people may have a misplaced confidence in their government; they may feel that it would not permit the continued sale of a product that was truly lethal.

Dr. Alvin M. Weinberg, director of the Oak Ridge National Laboratory, pointed out in a *Science* editorial (July 21, 1972):

> Many of the issues that lie at the interface between science and politics involve questions that can be stated in scientific terms but that are beyond the proficiency of science to answer. . . . For example, the biological effect on humans of very low level radiation (or of other physical insult, for that matter) will probably never be fully ascertained, simply because of the huge numbers of animals required to demonstrate an unequivocal effect. When the physical assault is on human lungs, then the transfer of animal data to humans blurs the validity of whatever laboratory data emerge.

The recent passage of the National Environmental Policy Act (NEPA) served to formalize the nation's concern with

19

the quality of the environment. Section 102 of this act is turning out to have a powerful effect on federal action in the control of many forms of pollution. Each agency of government is required to file with the Council on Environmental Quality a 102 statement detailing the environmental impact of programs and projects under its jurisdiction, as well as listing alternatives to the proposed course of action. This requirement has forced governmental agencies to look more closely at technologies and policies that could impair the quality of our air, soil, and water. For example, when the Trans-Alaska Pipeline System proposed to pump oil from the North Slope down to the port of Valdez, the Department of the Interior was required to submit a 102 impact statement and to solicit the comments of other agencies. In the process, this statement becomes a public document and is available to the interested citizen or citizen group. The door is opened to public criticism of a proposed federal action *prior to* implementation of the program.

In the case of TAPS (Trans-Alaska Pipeline System), it is rather clear that the people of Alaska and the U.S. Department of the Interior were not looking for data to challenge a decision to build the oil link. The allure of cash flow from the oil fields and the political pressure developed by oil company interests were more than a match for the opposition of environmentalists. Thus the 102 statement was only a tool for intervenors and not a truly effective mechanism for bringing about an objective evaluation of the issues. Where science and politics collide, the latter is apt to carry the most momentum. The basic dilemma in the area of techno-politics is that technologists are in an advisory position, whereas politicians are decision makers.

The 102 impact statement is a potent innovation in a democratic decision-making process, since it ventilates an issue publicly and thus allows for public intervention. But it is true that many federal inquiries have a high technological content that may be way over the head of the average citizen. As Theodore Roszak observed in his book *The Making of a Counter Culture:*

> In the technocracy, nothing is any longer small or simple or readily apparent to the non-technical man. Instead, the scale and intricacy of human activities—political, economic, cultural—transcends the competence of the amateurish citizen and inexorably demands the attention of specially trained experts. . . .
> In the technocracy everything aspires to become purely technical, the subject of professional attention. The technocracy is therefore the regime of experts—or of those who employ the experts.

Such a technicalization of public issues tends to convert the government of a democracy into an authoritarian overlord who decides what is good for the populace. There can be no doubt that the man in the street is easily bewildered by the onrush of progress. Those in our society who are professionally competent must speak out on issues where society and technology are in collision and must challenge federal, state, or local action. The forces arrayed against such intervention seem at first overwhelming, but a determined and skillful opposition can succeed. Certainly, one is hard put to conceive of a more difficult confrontation than that of the layman versus the nuclear-power plant. The latter is a consummately complex development of modern technology masterminded by a special government agency, the U.S. Atomic Energy Commission (AEC), and dominated by some of the nation's largest corporations and utilities. Yet beginning in 1970 intervenors challenged the safety and the siting of nuclear-power installations and forced the AEC and the nuclear industry to make a complete reevaluation of the basic tenets of nuclear safety.

Later on I will introduce many examples of logarithmic growth in production and consumption, but I will begin by focusing on energy sources that fuel the economy. These examples will concern the United States, because this country is the front-runner in world technology and it is here that the rates of growth have been most marked. In our final chapter, however, the worldwide implications of logarithmic growth will be considered.

21

Other nations, some with fewer natural resources and less real estate than the United States, will try to follow in the footsteps of the technological giant. Those like Canada, with a small population and huge untapped resources, will be less troubled by the impact of unrelenting growth; but Canada will have to pursue a prudent conservation policy lest its future be mortgaged by the excessive demands of its all-consuming neighbor to the south. European countries—Belgium and Holland, to name a pair—have limited *lebensraum* and finite natural resources. For them, continued growth will mean expert planning. Such nations will indeed be interested, as will France, Italy, and others, in observing how the United States manages to husband its resources and protect its environment.

I highlight energy—its relationship to the economy and to the environment—because its production represents by far the greatest source of pollution in the United States and because at the same time it is so fundamental to growth and so determining in setting our life-style. If we take the word *economy* to mean household management, then *ecology* is very much the same, except that it expands to include continental and planetary management. The preservation of the ecology is very much a contest between the perturbing forces of man and the corrective reaction of nature.

This book is really about a conjunction of sciences—ecology and economics, or *eco-economics.*

CHAPTER

2

HELL ON WHEELS

When the Honorable Charles E. Wilson, Eisenhower's first secretary of defense, complacently averred in 1955, "What's good for General Motors is good for the country," most Americans regarded the statement as an unremarkable truism. The feeble outcry it provoked from a few eggheads only baffled them. As the General Motors president-on-leave, Mr. Wilson considered his now-notorious aphorism as no more than a commonsense answer to questions about the propriety of his retaining large stockholdings in a corporation whose interests might be in conflict with the interests of the public-at-large. Didn't everybody know that the sales records of General Motors, the country's largest corporation, were an infallible index of the nation's economic health? And if a nation was expanding economically, what else could possibly matter?

Fifteen years were to elapse before the man in the street began to see the fallacy of the argument. By then he was living out his days in a miasma of effluents that bore a direct relationship to GM's affluence, and he began to add his own voice to the protesting egghead chorus. As an all-too-obvious technogiant, the automobile industry's lack of foresight was to contribute to the rise of anti-technology in the United States. As Professor Jurgen Schmandt expressed it in a *Science* editorial (October 15, 1971): "A period of faith in science and technology as an engine of social progress has come to an end. The power of knowledge to anticipate undesirable effects of technological change and to trigger corrective action has been questioned." Detroit's engines of progress roared onward unmindful of the consequences of resource depletion in our petroleum fields or of pollution via the tailpipe.

No single technological development has yet matched the impact of the internal-combustion engine on the life-style and economy of the United States. Once unleashed upon a quasi-defenseless society, the automobile proved to be a invincible chariot—a weapon, a status symbol, a dreamboat, a Madison Avenue delight, a bellwether of the economy, a time-payment bonanza, and a resurfacer of the American land.

The bicycle built for two and the horse-drawn buggy or tram were upstaged at Madison Square Garden in 1900 when thirty-one exhibitors displayed their wares at an automobile show. Eight electric drives and an equal number of steamers were shown off, but the petroleum-powered models swept aside the competition. Within two years the Oldsmobile was being mass-produced at the rate of over 2,000 cars per year as the chain-driven, tiller-steered paragon achieved popularity with its 5-horsepower engine and 20-mile-per-hour performance. The Model T was introduced by Henry Ford in 1908, and the first of 15 million monochrome "tin lizzies" hit the highways. America's ever-increasing enchantment with four-wheeled, rubber-tired mobility is illustrated in Figure 2-1. World War I cut automobile production back, but, even so, vehicle registrations totaled 10 million as the roaring twenties began.

My own family was caught up in the car craze and was in fact dependent upon it. My father worked as a machinist for the Pierce-Arrow Motor Car Company, so we had our own captive repairman on the great day in 1924 when we bought our first car—a shiny black Chevy. A touring sedan with no heater and with removable isinglass windows, the family car gave the Lapps a new sense of mobility. I still remember the heady excitement of a two-day drive from Buffalo, New York, to Washington, D.C. This 400-mile trip featured an unexpected diversion as my mother drove us into the shallows of the Susquehanna River.

It must have been obvious to even the most exuberant car salesman that the great automobile boom of the first two decades could not continue. After all, sighting up the car registration curve along a straight line drawn for the 1900–1920 period (Fig. 2-1) projected 100 million cars by 1926 and a billion by 1933. Of course, this was an absurdity, and new car sales tilted over after World War I, reaching a peak of 5 million units just before the Great Crash of 1929. At the time of the Crash, motor registrations included 23 million autos, along with some 3.5 million trucks and buses; the vehicles consumed 15 billion gallons of motor fuel per year.

Apparently, the horsepower binge in Detroit is ending; there is now a limit to engine size. The V-8 has long been the American favorite. In 1970 the V-8 commanded 84 percent of U.S. production providing the average 292 horsepower, which served not just to propel the auto down the highway but to power an increasing surfeit of gadgets within the car itself. Nine of every ten motorcars featured automatic transmission and only slightly fewer came equipped with power steering, while two of every three passenger cars were air-conditioned. A car without a radio was so rare as to constitute some kind of sales mistake. Americans not only want to drive fast but want to travel with all the comforts of home.

If federal authorities were to crack down on automotive horsepower, either because of the pollution it causes or because of the need to conserve fuel, fuel consumption would begin to fall significantly below the mileage curve.

Until very recently Detroit has designed and engineered its cars without much thought of the need to conserve gasoline or to abate the air pollution caused by the daily traffic in metropolitan areas. Auto makers now face a 1975–76 deadline for compliance with an act of Congress regulating exhaust emissions, but they believe the regulations can be met without cutting back the power of the V-8s. As yet there is little to indicate that gasoline will be in such short supply as to require restraint on engine size, but limits seem to have been reached in automobile dimensions and performance.

On February 10, 1970, President Nixon announced the start of a new attack on vehicular pollution:

> I am inaugurating a program to marshal both Government and private research with the goal of producing an unconventionally powered, virtually pollution-free automobile within 5 years.

FIGURE 2-1

U.S. MOTOR-VEHICLE SALES AND REGISTRATIONS

The top line represents the growth of private ownership of cars and trucks, as determined by the count of recorded registrations. The bottom line charts new-car sales. The American compulsion to keep rolling, come hell or high water, is evidenced by the negligible dips in the top line when new-car sales sagged precipitously during the Depression and when they actually plunged below the pre–World War I level during the World War II freeze on sales of all but essential vehicles. A chart of old-car rehabilitations would, of course, show corresponding peaks.

FIGURE 2-1

U.S. MOTOR-VEHICLE SALES
AND REGISTRATIONS

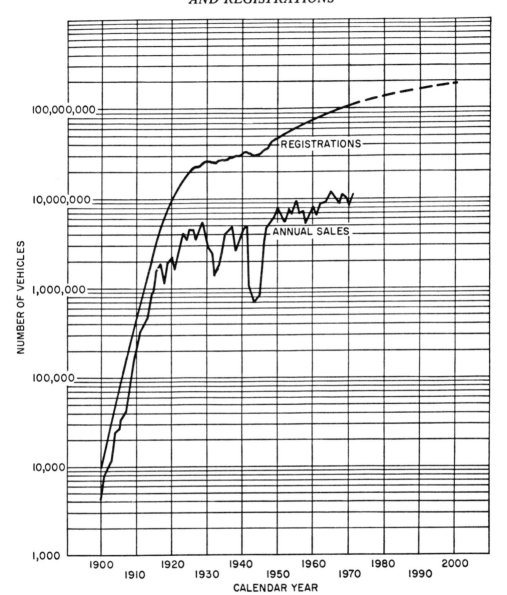

In his May 1971 report, William D. Ruckelshaus, administrator of the Environmental Protection Agency, enumerated the engine systems "which appear to have the greatest potential for becoming viable alternatives to the conventional internal-combustion engine." The EPA chief listed the gas turbine, the heat-electric hybrid, and the Rankine cycle engine. The gas turbine has been under development for some time, but its emission of nitrogen oxides is troublesome and its high capital cost is a drawback. In any event the turbine

FIGURE 2-2

MOTOR-VEHICLE DATA

The Depression put a slight crimp in motor-vehicle travel (upper line), but it took the gasoline curbs of World War II (center line) to cause it to stagger. Otherwise the two (naturally parallel) lines for miles and gallons march onward and upward with monotonous regularity. The trend seems likely to continue for at least another twenty years; there is no likelihood that the internal-combustion engine will cease to dominate the roadways before 1990. By that time, total vehicular traffic will probably have reached 1.7 trillion miles. (For convenience, the scales of the two curves have been adjusted. Values for miles are on the left of the graph; values for gallons are on the right.)

The lethality of the automobile is pinpointed by the death statistics which continue to pile up despite the innovation of safety devices and highway safety engineering.

FIGURE 2-2

MOTOR-VEHICLE DATA

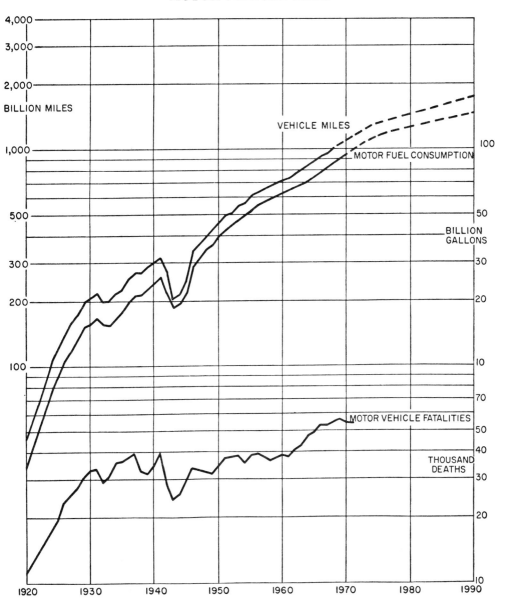

will demand petroleum as fuel, although it can be kerosene-type rather than gasoline. The hybrid is an attempt to over-come the drawbacks of the electric car, whose performance does not match the V-8's. For long hauls and high perform-ance, the hybird would depend on a turbine or an internal-combustion engine; for low speed and short range it would switch over to battery drive. The Rankine engine is essen-tially the steam engine. So, in effect, after seventy years we go back to the three classes of vehicles exhibited at the Madi-son Square Garden auto show in 1900. The Wankel engine—an internal-combustion engine that has replaced pistons with rotors—is an improvement over the V-8. It delivers power for two-thirds of its combustion phases as against only one-fourth for the piston engine. And it can digest lead-free low-octane gasoline without loss of power or economy. The Japa-nese Mazda Wankel-equipped auto is now available in the United States, and Ford and General Motors have bought rights to the Wankel.

Whatever pollution-free vehicle emerges from EPA's de-velopment program, it must meet the test of the marketplace. Federal authorities are unlikely to outlaw the V-8 summarily, although they might limit its power and decree production of a brand-new kind of engine. General Motors ranks as the No. 1 U.S. corporation and has a 1971 sales total of $28.3 billion for 56 percent of the car market, with Ford as the runner-up with a sales total of $16.5 billion and Chrysler a poor third with $8 billion. Together with other manufactur-ers, the U.S. motor-vehicle production in 1971 added up to $55 billion and loomed even larger in the nation's economy because of associated sales and services. The impact of the automobile is only hinted at in new-car sales figures; if we count car upkeep, oil and gas, finance charges, insurance, and tires on passenger cars alone, the grand total of expendi-tures was about $100 billion in 1971. Intercity trucking, em-ploying 9 million employees and having a $56 billion annual payroll, moved 600 million tons of freight in 1971.

There are other items to be included in tallying the cost of the internal-combustion engine—the human death toll in accidents, the paving over of much of the American landscape, the sheer agony of traffic jams, the unholy din of pounding tires and roaring engines, and the chemical warfare waged by 100 million tailpipes.

Henry H. Blaine, a sixty-eight-year-old real-estate broker in Manhattan, became America's first automobile casualty when he stepped off a streetcar on September 13, 1899. He was run down by a car at Seventy-fourth Street and Central Park West and died shortly thereafter. Figure 2-2 shows how the motorcar became an instrument of lethality in American life. Motor-vehicle fatalities in 1971 totaled 55,000, and I prayerfully refrain from projecting this death curve into the future. In the past half-century, traffic accidents have killed 1.76 million Americans, or more than twice the battle deaths of all Americans in all U.S. history.

The extent of the inroads made by the motorcar on America's landscape should be apparent from Figure 2-3. Yet the construction program has not alleviated the woes of the commuter who braves rush-hour traffic to get from the suburbs to the city. Far too often, expressways become parking lots as exasperated drivers are stalled in bumper-to-bumper jam-ups. Aggravating the situation, parking in the central cities has become a nightmare.

Naturally, the care and feeding of 100 million vehicles requires a vast empire of service stations, tire shops, and parts departments. A lack of urban planning and a complete disregard for aesthetics have led to an unsightly sprawl of gas stations, some 220,000 of them at last count, which contribute to making American cities uniformly ugly. Used-car lots and hideous automotive cemeteries disfigure almost every U.S. city, town, and village.

Air pollution by cars and trucks was not subjected to federal regulation for two-thirds of this century. Not until 1968 did the Department of Health, Education, and Welfare impose controls on crankcase hydrocarbons, and on the hydrocarbons and carbon monoxide (CO) emitted by auto tailpipes. Carbon monoxide is the most massive pollutant; a peak of 62 million tons was emitted in 1967–68—quite a gas attack for a society to launch against itself. Fortunately, the application of emission standards to new cars promises to drop the CO discharge to about 17 million tons per year by 1985. After that, barring more stringent regulations, the curve will rise again as millions of new cars are put on the roads.

A great deal of public attention has focused on population control, with emphasis on contraception; but few have seen the need for applying the contraceptive approach to

FIGURE 2-3

STATE HIGHWAY EXPENDITURES

The growth in the quantities of money allotted by the states to highway building since 1920 parallels the increase in new-car sales (Fig. 2-1), with corresponding dips during the 1930s (the Depression) and the 1940s (World War II). Since the war, the states have spent more than $200 billion in a massive effort to expedite the country's traffic.

FIGURE 2-3

STATE HIGHWAY EXPENDITURES

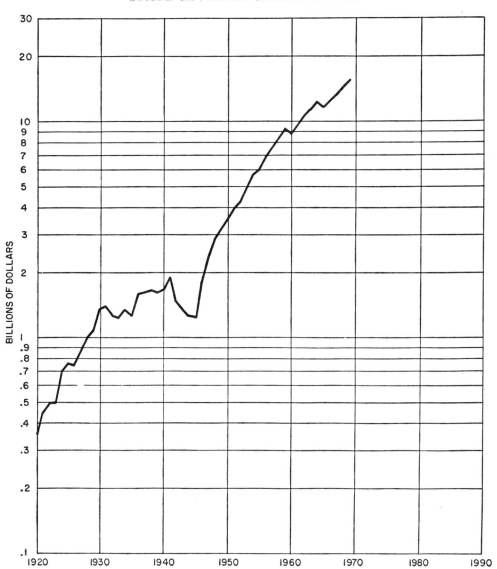

automobiles. Motorcar production is limited only by the cus-tomers' ability to pay or by their willingness and ability to pass a credit examination. If we can consider cutting back on people at the source, then it would seem as legitimate to contemplate birth control of America's most lethal mechani-cal invention. (Bermuda is one place that practices family planning of its motorcar population.) There are, to be sure, certain natural limitations to the ultimate car population. In Figure 2-1 the extrapolation to the year 2000 assumes that no American will drive more than one car at a time, but he may well *own* more than one. Conceivably, if the hybrid engine of EPA does not work out or satisfy the public, those who can afford it will own two cars each, one to drive into the city (an electric charge-at-home model) and another to cruise about the country (a fossil-fueled model). In any event, I have projected a total vehicle mileage (Fig. 2-2) that tapers off during the next several decades. All vehicular traffic in the year 2000 should approach 2 trillion miles.

No matter how it is figured, 2 trillion miles of travel will require a very large energy input. To curb pollution, we may go to electricity or some other form of motive power, but any fuel switch constitutes an energy switch that must be fully reckoned in the nation's account books. For example, natural gas is a low-pollutant fuel that can be adapted to automotive systems. But fueling 100 million motorcars with natural gas would require more than 10 trillion cubic feet (Tcf) per year—almost half the present total U.S. consumption. As we shall see in the next chapter, natural gas threatens to be in short supply unless it can be synthesized from solid fuels, such as coal. If, on the other hand, we switch from gasoline to electricity, we throw an additional load on the nation's electric-energy-generating capacity. Of course, electric utilities must use *some* fuel to produce heat to generate steam to turn turbines; this fuel, whether fossil or nuclear, must be reck-oned as a national energy expenditure.

Besides, the sheer magnitude of our industrial investment

34

in the V-8 argues against any rapid phase-out of gasoline-driven engines. The futurizing of motor-fuel consumption in Figure 2-2 is therefore a realistic though an optimistic one. It assumes a reversal of the recent trend, that is, that miles-per-gallon will actually rise during the next twenty years, leading to a 160-billion-gallon gasoline consumption in 1990. (The oilman's unit of production is the barrel, standardized at 42 gallons, so our 1990 figure comes to almost 4 billion barrels of gasoline.)

Crude oil is the natural form of petroleum that gasoline is derived from. It takes about nine barrels of crude to yield four barrels of gasoline; this means a resource requirement of 9 million barrels of crude oil to supply our 1990 gasoline production. Will that much crude be available? Let us examine the petroleum reserves in the continental United States—meaning the lower forty-eight states, and offshore and Alaskan reserves.

The U.S. oil ledger may be seen as a system of deposits and withdrawals: a known oil reserve is built up through extensive exploratory drilling and is then depleted year by year. Figure 2-4 illustrates this buildup and rundown over the past half-century.

In banker's terms, we are drawing on our capital to an increasing extent. While this may not be foolhardy for an old person who is near death and has little desire to leave a large estate, it is profligate for a government that must consider the mobility of future generations—unless, of course, it plans some other energy source for propulsion.

Our oil capital, or proved reserves, is shown in Figure 2-4 as the topmost curve.. The relation between the reserve (R) and the production (P) statistics, expressed as a fraction R/P, is of critical importance. Imagine that all the oil reserves of the United States are contained in a single large vessel. New discoveries represent additions to the vessel, causing the level of oil to rise, while production from oil wells corresponds to a hole in the container, causing the liquid level to drop. U.S. demand for oil, the source of 44 percent of all energy in this country, continues unabated, an ever-widening hole in the bottom of the imaginary oil barrel. To supply this oil, the United States is pumping its more than half million wells at near capacity, thus pushing the R/P ratio from a "comfortable" 10:1 to a more perilous 8:1 ratio. An R/P of 8:1 means that, barring further additions to reserves and a constant annual consumption, our oil supply will last eight years.

FIGURE 2-4

U.S. CRUDE-OIL CONSUMPTION AND PRODUCTION

A bend-over in the curve of proved crude-oil reserves since 1959 (top line) is apparent. (Proved reserves of crude oil are those that geologic and engineering data demonstrate with reasonable certainty to be recoverable from known reservoirs under existing economic conditions. Not shown are some 23 billion barrels discovered before 1920 and known to be ultimately recoverable.) In the meanwhile, consumption has climbed steadily since the leveling off (center line). Oil production from U.S. fields has also climbed (bottom line), but not as rapidly as consumption, and is expected to decline alarmingly beginning about 1975 (dotted line).

FIGURE 2-4

U.S. CRUDE-OIL CONSUMPTION
AND PRODUCTION

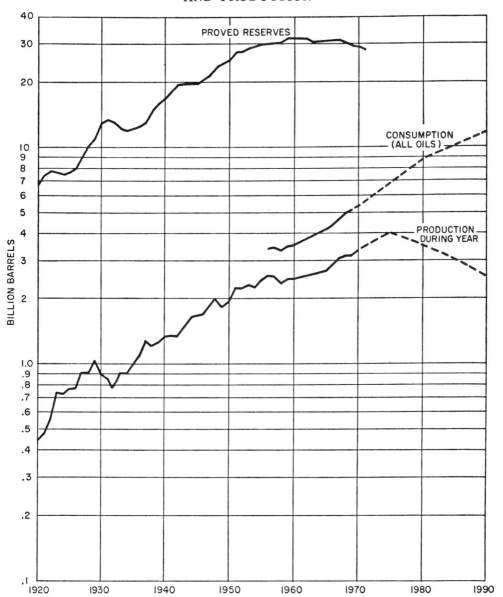

To be sure, more oil remains to be found, both within our borders and offshore, but an increasing population and, more important, an increased per capita demand cause this fuel to flow out of our hypothetical barrel faster than it flows in. How much oil remains to be discovered in America? In the past, oilmen have assured their critics that there is plenty of oil yet to be discovered and have argued that they need incentives (depletion allowances) to spend the money required to find it. However, the surface of the United States has been probed with almost 2 million drill holes; it is no longer an unknown quantity. In fact, it is so well explored that oil companies prefer to spend their money looking for oil offshore, in Alaska, or elsewhere.

The great oil finds of the 1920s and 1930s, measured in terms of barrels found per foot of well drilled, are a far cry from today's results. There has been a sixfold drop in their discovery rate since then, and of course each foot drilled today is far more expensive than in the oil-boom days. Experts estimate that ultimate U.S. recovery will amount to about 200 billion barrels of crude oil. Some specialists put the value as low as 165 billion barrels, and others think it might be as high as 300 billion. Computation of the rate at which this great pool of oil may be tapped produces an estimate of about 4 billion barrels per year early in this decade. Using a model developed by oil experts, I have charted the next two decades of crude-oil production as a dotted line in Figure 2-4. This is really a horrifying projection: It predicts a peaking of domestic production in a very few years, followed by a gradual decline. By 1990 the United States will be pumping only as much petroleum as it did in 1960. Remember that we projected *9 billion* barrels of crude oil as the amount needed to supply U.S. transportation requirements in 1990. We will be producing only about 2.5 billion barrels. The picture is even grimmer when we realize that petroleum is also used for needs other than motor fuel, and not all of these are met by using the distillates remaining when gasoline is topped off the distilling columns.

The total production of oil from U.S. fields to date amounts to almost 100 billion barrels. In other words, if we accept the estimate of 200 billion barrels as ultimately recoverable, then the United States has already exploited half its total petroleum inheritance. Where, then, will it obtain the oil to satisfy its mounting demand—the "consumption" rate projected in Figure 2-4 based on recent State Department figures? One answer is obvious: About one-fourth of U.S.-consumed oil (including petroleum liquids) is imported. Most of this comes from Canada and Venezuela, but increasing amounts are being supplied by the oil-drenched Middle East. In 1970 a total of 483 million barrels of crude oil was imported, about half of this from Canada and a fifth from Venezuela. Crude-oil imports are tightly controlled by the U.S. government, but residual oil is being imported in increasing quantities, totaling 577 million barrels in 1970.

Are world oil resources adequate to supply U.S. demands in the future? Naturally, this depends on the oil demands made by European and other nations. Here is a recent estimate of proved reserves made by the State Department's Office of Fuels and Energy:

Arab Middle East and North Africa	350 billion barrels
Iran	60
U.S. (including Alaska)	40
Venezuela	15
Indonesia	15
Canada	10
Other Western Hemisphere	10
Other African	5
Others	5
Total	510 billion barrels

This is actually a conservative estimate, crediting Saudi Arabia with 150 billion barrels, though many experts believe the figure may be twice that. Moreover, these represent proved reserves and do not allow for new discoveries. It is very probable that immense quantities of oil are locked up in Arctic areas and offshore regions. On the other side of the ledger, the world is consuming petroleum at rates that the State Department predict will climb as follows:

	1970	1980	1990	2000	
Consumption by non-Communist world	15	30	44	58	Billion barrels per year

It seems clear that liquid fuels taken from the earth will peak in consumption some time before this century's end and will then decline as reserves are exhausted and new fields fail to open up for exploitation.

For the oil-producing countries of the Middle East there is relatively little domestic demand for their product, and it is available for as low as its $0.10 a barrel production cost. By way of contrast, Texas oil in 1971 sold for $3.40 at the wellhead. With U.S. production slated to peak in a few years, it seems inevitable that the gap between U.S. supply and demand will have to be met by importing oil from the Middle East. A number of U.S. oil industrialists believe that by 1985 as much as three-fifths of U.S. oil will be imported and that the bulk of this will come from Persian Gulf nations. Six of these, Abu Dhabi, Iran, Iraq, Kuwait, Qatar, and Saudi Arabia, are members of OPEC—Organization of Petroleum Exporting Countries—which recently presented a united bargaining front to such international oil companies as Standard Oil of New Jersey, British Petroleum, Royal Dutch, and Texaco. They were able to win higher prices for oil, and if the United States were to become *dependent* upon OPEC for oil, it would perforce be at the mercy of price escalations in the future.

The combination of larger fuel imports and higher prices for premium fuels is a potential destabilizer for the U.S. balance of payments, leading to top-heavy trade deficits. There do not appear to be exportable products capable of righting this imbalance, and AEC chairman Dr. James R. Schlesinger has estimated that the 1980 oil imports, reckoned at 1972 prices, could involve an outpayment of $15 billion. Any projection to 1990 or 2000 would necessarily involve both greater volumes of oil and considerably higher prices, so that dependence on foreign oil really becomes economically prohibitive.

What can the United States do to become self-sufficient in oil? First, it can exploit its offshore potential more fully, although this does not appear to hold much promise. Second, it can turn northward to Alaska where the North Slope has reserves of at least 10 billion barrels and possibly twice that. The difficulty here is in transporting the oil across some 800 miles of land to the port of Valdez. The Trans-Alaska Pipeline System (TAPS) has been violently opposed as a threat to the ecology of the land area, and the Valdez-to-U.S. route for oil tankers is so hazardous that there would be a constant danger of oil spills from ships that are damaged or run aground in foul weather. The single TAP 48-inch pipeline would carry only 2 million barrels per day (0.7 billion barrels per year, but a 1.5 million barrel-per-day capacity is the maximum planned for the seventh year of operation and the theoretical maximum may never be attained), and even if a twin pipeline is installed, would move no more than 1.4 billion barrels per year to the lower forty-eight states. While significant now, this amount of petroleum would be only a small fraction of the U.S. demand in 1990. If, however, substantial finds are made offshore in the Arctic, we might want to put priority on Arctic oil recovery. Still, there would be the problem of an eco-safe system for bringing it south.

Oil is the mainstay of the U.S. energy economy, and it is not easy to make fuel switches quickly. Add to this the projected growth for the consumption of fuels, and it is difficult to see how the United States can remain self-sufficient in its oil economy. Consider, for example, that 250 billion barrels of petroleum may be estimated to be required for the rest of the century. The United States has no liquid reserves in prospect in the contiguous forty-eight states, off-shore, or in Alaska to satisfy such a demand. However, we do have solid fuels—coal, oil shale, and tar sands—in great abundance, and these can be transformed into oil through liquefaction or synthesis. (Their abundance and methods of liquefaction will be discussed in the next chapter.) Of course, converting these solids into liquids on a scale to match U.S. consumption of petroleum by the end of the century will not be easy. Unless almost all the experts are wrong, U.S. demand for liquid fuel will then approach 15 billion barrels per year.

If synthesis of liquid fuel does not exceed the supply of domestic oil reserves in the year 2000 and the latter remains at today's level, then the United States will be importing 10 billion barrels or more of oil per year. This would mean dependence on a fleet of supertankers, most of which would probably carry several million barrels per trip. One accident at sea could spill more than 100 million gallons of oil into the ocean.

Brutal economics force reliance on supertankers in the quarter-million-ton or larger class when they have to make the 14,000-mile trip from the Persian Gulf to U.S. ports. Yet, on the receiving end, only Seattle can accommodate the 67- to 70-foot (some supertankers run 81-foot) draught of these immense ships. The United States is considering building a $1.3 billion deepwater terminal or artificial harbor-island nine miles off Cape Henlopen, Delaware. The 500-acre sea terminal would handle 300 million tons of oil a year and would permit tanker docking up to 325,000 tons deadweight. Apart from the threat to the ecology, the import program would drain off American dollars and seriously affect the balance of payments. This dollar drain would be exacerbated by rising oil prices as the oil sheiks of OPEC drive harder and harder bargains in future negotiations. It seems inevitable that we must either switch from liquid fuels to alternative energy sources or curtail our fuel consumption.

The United States is, then, approaching the limits of its growth, unless we devise a technology that circumvents the barriers imposed by shrinking natural resources and growing environmental disruption. Nonrenewable fuel resources, such as petroleum, are the heritage of our planet's storing up of solar energy in the age of the dinosaurs. The price of mobility has simply not been calculated in a country where a car owner's casual "Fill 'er up" means converting a full barrel of crude oil into horsepower and airborne hydrocarbons.

Given the galloping nature of human demands on nature's limited storehouse of fossil fuels, it would appear that Vice Admiral H. G. Rickover's following observation is all too true. Commenting on America's exploitation of nonrenewable resources, Admiral Rickover observed in 1972:

> . . . we are faced with the fact that while it took 600 millennia to create the earth's deposits of fossil fuels, we are using them up in a time span measured by decades. . . . The Fossil Fuel Age may well prove to have been one of the briefest major epochs in man's long history on earth.

Logarithmic growth sooner or later gets a society into trouble. In one way or another this growth intrudes upon the nation, buffeting its ecology, or its resources, or simply filling up the space available within and even above its borders. A case in point is the spectacular rise in air transportation as shown in Fig. 2-5. The changeover to the jet engine which burns kerosene-type fuels, instead of high-octane gasoline, eased the fuel economy somewhat. Present aircraft fuel consumption, primarily of jet fuel, runs to roughly 200 million barrels per year. This is modest compared with the more than 2 billion barrels used by our automobiles, but the rate of increase is impressive. Were it to continue in the pattern of the past two decades, we would have to extrapolate a 1-billion-barrel fuel consumption in 1980.

But, in projecting the future of air travel, we must take certain limiting factors into account. Getting to the airport, parking, waiting on the runway, stacking over the destination, and terminal delays add up to self-inflicted misery that can only discourage the air traveler. Jet liners streaking across the country at 600 miles per hour must often circle interminably once they are sucked into the traffic vortex above the major airports. Air space becomes inadequate to support the increased congestion, and metropolitan areas face the unhappy prospect of building even more remote airports for air travelers.

FIGURE 2-5

AIR TRANSPORTATION

The Depression notwithstanding, airline travel took off in the 1930s and has climbed almost steadily since. Its doubling time before World War II was less than six years. Doubling time in the 1960s lengthened to nine years, still an 8 percent annual increase. Fuel consumed in domestic air travel is plotted on the lower line, keyed to the scale at right. International air traffic increases the quantity by about 30 percent.

FIGURE 2-5

AIR TRANSPORTATION

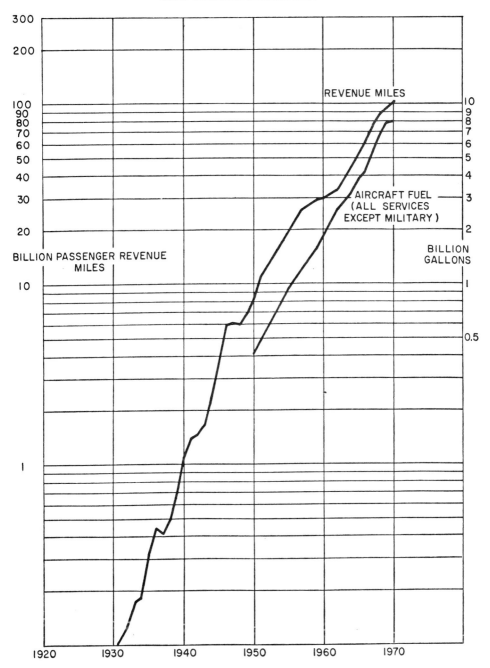

Belatedly, attempts have been made to speed travelers between cities; for example, between Washington and New York a metroliner railroad system of modest velocity has been established. But, in general, federal funding of mass-transportation systems has lagged behind the capital expenditures in behalf of the automobile and hard-surface travel. Our transportation policy must change to make resource conservation and environmental integrity prime considerations. Federal support of interstate highways has heretofore promoted the use of automobiles for long-distance travel, but federal planners ought to analyze the transportation options available, taking into account the need to conserve fossil fuels and minimize air pollution. Table 2-1 summarizes data on some modern transportation systems.

TABLE 2-1

MODERN TRANSPORTATION SYSTEMS

Description	Number of Passengers	Speed (mph)	Fuel Consumption	
			Pounds per hour	Pounds per Passenger Mile
Concorde	112	1,200	75,000	0.58
Ocean liner	2,000	38	76,000	1.0
Piston plane	65	320	2,300	0.11
Medium jet	110	550	11,000	0.17
Boeing 747	400	600	22,400	0.09
Diesel train	350	65	3,000	0.13
Cadillac	1	65	36	0.55
Volkswagen	4	65	16	0.06
Commuter bus	50	15	35	0.05

Transportation choices based solely on fuel consumption reckoned in pounds per passenger mile clearly lead to a Volkswagenized society or to group riding. But a fully loaded Greyhound bus would be even more fuel conserving. Obviously, the personal choice is rarely based on fuel conservation alone. If high-speed surface systems were chosen solely on a minimum-pollution basis, then electric-powered trains supplied with nuclear-generated electricity would predominate. Our transportation choices actually depend on a random mix of many factors in which personal control of a vehicle ranks very high. Most people, given the financial means, prefer the flexibility of their own automobile to mass-transit systems; but this has become too often a Hobson's choice.

The prolonged debate over the supersonic transport (SST) exposed some new wrinkles in man's increasing interaction with his environment and with the finiteness of his planet. The case for the SST rested largely on its use for intercontinental travel where the speed of 1,800 miles per hour abridged time and brought Australia, for example, many hours closer to the United States. But supersonic flight did little to bring Los Angeles closer to New York; all it offered was a marginal time gain that promised to desynchronize the body's time clock even more than the subsonic planes do. But the SST had its drawbacks for many millions of surface dwellers who would be exposed to the thunder-rumble of the aircraft overhead. I once saw government projections of the ground coverage by SST air shock. Fifty-mile-wide swaths, representing sound shadows, covered almost every square mile of North America except for a small corner of Nevada. In addition, the SST posed an alarming potential planetary threat: Some scientists maintained that it would disturb the ozone concentration of the stratosphere, allowing more ultraviolet radiation to pour down on the earth. This, some held, could cause a significant increase in skin cancer. The evidence, though far from convincing, shows how the earth is growing more vulnerable in hitherto unsuspected ways to man's technological tinkering.

When the century dawned, man was just developing the automobile and managing to match the speed of steam locomotives. By taking to the air he quickly increased the tempo of change from one locale to another, giving the traveler today an average twentyfold higher travel speed than in 1900. Figure 2-6 illustrates this progression. In time, no doubt, supersonic and even hypersonic aircraft will be adapted to commercial travel; but it is clear that there are practical limits to speed in moving about on or above the

FIGURE 2-6

MAN'S MOBILITY

In little more than a century, the rate of speed at which man can be carried about has increased tenfold for terrestrial passengers and four hundredfold for astronauts. The limit on speed for suborbital aircraft is 18,000 miles per hour. The fastest plane now in use—the Concorde—flies at 1,200 miles per hour. The space shuttle, approved in 1972, will limit man to orbital flight until 1990. The scattered progression of points marking man's ascent to swiftness appears to have reached a nature-imposed limit which is keyed to the physical characteristics of the solar system.

Man's alacrity is illustrated in Fig. 2-6 where his vehicular velocity is plotted with Xs marking the debut of milestones in locomotion. What is not shown is the increasing energy cost of man's mobility, although it is partly revealed in Table 2-1 on modern transportation systems.

FIGURE 2-6

MAN'S MOBILITY

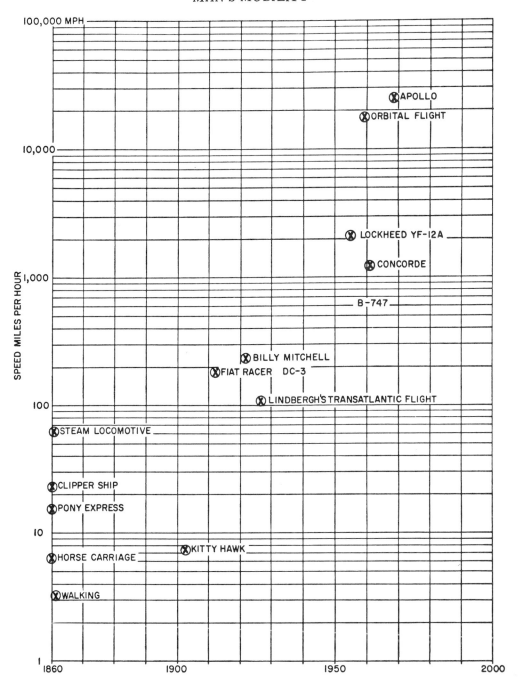

earth. There is, of course, the ultimate limit of 18,000 miles per hour, a speed that puts man into orbit, and with an added boost, takes him off into the darkness of space.

The speed of 25,000 miles per hour, known as "escape velocity," must be attained by astronauts taking off for the moon. Still higher velocities are needed for interplanetary trips. Whether or not trips into orbit or even deeper into space will ever be within the purchasing power of the average person is doubtful. Getting things from the earth's surface out into orbit requires enormous thrust, lifting very considerable weights. This is pure work, according to the laws of physics. The world's most prodigious weight lifter is the Saturn-V, the booster rocket for the Apollo craft. It can place in a low earth orbit as much as 275,000 pounds, but the cost per pound is $700.

There is under development a reusable space shuttle designed to cut the costs of earth-to-orbit traffic and bring them below $100 per pound. The space shuttle is in my opinion an example of technological politics or politicized technology. That is to say, it represents a technology sponsored for its political value—the shuttle was approved by the White House in 1972, a political year, not as an economically justifiable venture, but as an exercise in keeping a federal agency's budget up and in sustaining employment in the aerospace industries which are located in states of high presidential vote power. Designed as a vehicle to propel as much as 65,000 pounds into a low earth orbit, the shuttle is being programmed for 440 space missions in the 1978–90 time period. Such earth-to-orbit traffic ought to have some rational justification in terms of economic payoff, but very little evidence of such worth has been put forth. If each orbital mission carries an average of 15,000 pounds (ten times the 1960–70 average for unmanned missions), then a total of 6.6 million pounds of payload will be exported. Overall program costs for this space transportation including shuttle development, production, and operations will probably run about $15 billion, although major cost overruns may be anticipated. This means that the new shuttle system will average $2,400 per pound of payload placed in orbit—or 3.4 times as much as the present Saturn system cost. Clearly, we are dealing with orbital economics completely unhinged from realities on earth.

The concomitant upswing in horsepower, from 25 million hp in 1890 to 20 billion hp in 1970, represents an almost thousandfold increase in eighty years (Fig. 2-7). The character of this prime-mover power is reflected in Table 2-2, which compares energy sources of 1900 and 1970.

TABLE 2-2

PRIME MOVERS IN THE U.S. ECONOMY (1900 and 1970)

| Prime Mover | Horsepower | |
	1900	1970
Railroads	18.7 million	54 million
Work animals	24.5	1.3
Factories (power on site)	10.3	54
Human energy	4	10
Aircraft	0	183
Mines	2.9	45
Central electric plants	2.4	435
Merchant fleet	1.7	22
Motor vehicles	0.1	19,325
	64.6 million	20,129 million

The remarkable shift from beasts of burden as the largest source of power in 1900 to "horses under the hood" in 1970 truly reflects the motorization of America. The statistics indelibly underline the revolutionary significance of the internal-combustion engine in this century. Few charts and tables so vividly mark the change in man's ways as do the horsepower representations. They show the virtual elimination of the work animal and the shift to a wheeled society as well as to a jet-propelled mode of transportation. But even more they serve to indicate the evolution of our American life-style from a low-energy to a high-energy existence. So that we may better understand this radical transformation

FIGURE 2-7

GROWTH OF HORSEPOWER

The horsepower expended to keep America functioning has increased almost a thousandfold in the past eighty years. In 1970 the proportion of the total that was generated by motor vehicles dwarfed all the rest to a mere speck. (See Table 2-2.)

FIGURE 2-7

GROWTH OF HORSEPOWER

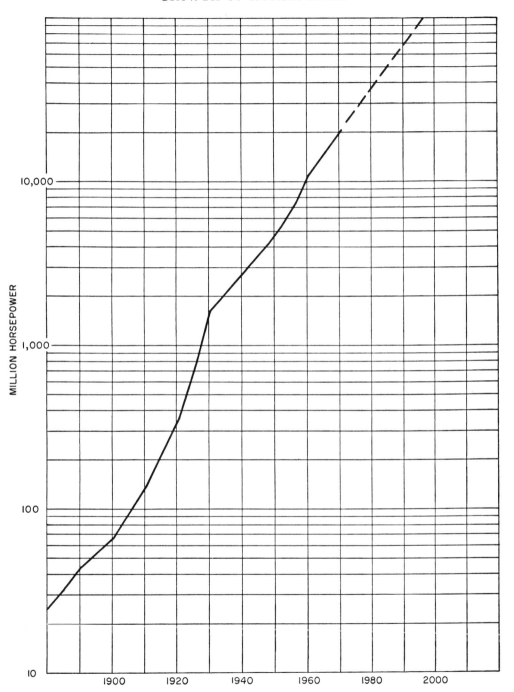

and its quantitative meaning, it is necessary to introduce some units of energy and power. Power is the rate of doing work. Energy is consumed in the performance of work. James Watt, the man who contributed so much to the development of a practical steam engine, gave us the definition of horsepower. In an experiment, he had a workhorse pull a heavy weight up from a well and measured the time it took for the weight to be lifted through a given height. In physics, *work* is defined as the product of the vertical distance lifted and the weight of the object. To hedge against contentious claims from farmers to whom he sold his engines, Watt added a 50 percent margin to his definition of the horsepower, making it equal to 550 foot-pounds per second.

A 180-pound man climbing a flight of stairs, elevating himself ten feet, does 1,800 foot-pounds of work. If ten seconds are required for the climb, then the work is done at the rate of 180 foot-pounds per second, and this divided by 550 makes the man's work equal to about one-third horsepower. Man, himself, rated as a machine working full time, is about 0.05 horsepower. The 60 million total prime-mover power of 1900 divided by the population of 76 million amounted to 0.8 horsepower per person. This meant that machines and beasts of burden had multiplied man's self-power by a factor of 16 in 1900. In 1970 each person had at his disposal, thanks largely to the automobile, 100 horsepower.

Modern man's power is obtained from the chemical energy of fossil fuels such as coal, natural gas, and petroleum, and he is just beginning to tame a new source of energy—the atom. Fossil fuels generate power as they are burned to produce heat which is then used to drive engines. The heat potential of a fossil fuel is expressed in British thermal units (BTUs), one "unit" being the amount of heat required to raise one pound of water one degree Fahrenheit. A ton of coal gives off about 26 million BTUs, and a barrel of petroleum is rated at 5.8 million BTUs. A gallon of gasoline is rated at 125,000 BTUs, and 1,000 cubic feet of natural gas yield 1,032,000 BTUs. These three fuel forms—liquid, solid, and gas—were the basis for the U.S. energy economy, supporting 95 percent of all U.S. energy needs in 1972. Hydroelectric power, with a small assist from nuclear power, accounted for most of the remaining 5 percent.

Having introduced the BTU as our unit of energy, we are now in a position to make preliminary explorations into the virgin field of what can be called "BTU economics." Economists traditionally worship at the altar of the gross national product, regarding the dollar sign as the index of national worth. As may be seen by comparing the shape of Figure 1-5, which displays the time growth of the GNP, with that of Figure 1-4, where the growth pattern of electric energy is illustrated, there is a striking correlation. Remembering that electric energy is a product of energy conversion which is achievable by burning fossil fuel, the kilowatt-hours in Figure 1-4 may be expressed in BTUs. In the next chapter we shall trace the growth of BTUs in more detail for the 1900–1970 period, but at this point we make a specific BTU analysis of the motorcar.

The 1972 GNP of $1.2 trillion may be correlated with an annual energy consumption of 75 quadrillion BTUs, so that $1 of GNP is equivalent to 62,500 BTUs. The U.S. government's *Statistical Abstract for 1971* lists the ten-year total cost of a four-door sedan costing $3,374 as about $10,000, not including gasoline charges. If we take our BTU/$ ratio given above, this means that the ten-year BTU cost of an automobile is 625 million BTUs. This figure is an understatement because the BTU/$ ratio is undoubtedly considerably higher for energy intensive production represented by the automobile. I would estimate that it is fair to say the BTU capital cost plus operations, minus fuel, of an automobile over a decade is 1 billion BTUs and probably considerably higher. Unfortunately, the state of BTU economics is such that we cannot be very precise on this point. Now to this accounting we must add the BTU costs of fuel. Reckoning an annual average of 800 gallons of gasoline at

125,000 BTUs per gallon yields 100 million BTUs, or 1 billion BTUs for a decade. Summing up, this means that every automobile represents a 2-billion-BTU energy commitment for the United States.

Since we have roughly 100 million motor vehicles on the road, this implies an annual BTU expenditure of 20 quadrillion BTUs, or over a fourth of the total U.S. energy expenditures. However, since U.S. motor vehicles are premium fuel users, the impact of personal mobility on the BTU economy is of critical importance. One way to dramatize the significance of the BTU and the automobile is to focus on a single commuter as he drives from the suburbs to the central city in his medium-class automobile. A 20-mile daily trek involves, by my reckoning, 500,000 BTUs, or about 25,000 BTUs per mile. This is one hundred times more BTU expenditure than pedaling a bicycle for one mile. Obviously the life-style of the gay nineties and the unnamed seventies is set in stark contrast.

The United States has paid little attention to BTUs in its national growth, but the requirements of mobility make it mandatory that high priority be attached to forward planning for meeting the U.S. energy needs. The automobile has fostered an urbanization and metropolitan sprawl of such dimensions that the U.S. population must be provided with a daily means of transportation from home to work, school, and shopping. Lacking suitable mass transit, it becomes essential to provide premium fuels for the growing multitude of motor vehicles and this, as we shall see, is a far-from-solved problem.

CHAPTER

3

THE GREAT BURNUP

Fuel and power have an egg-to-omelet relationship; it takes heat to produce energy. Until the advent of the atom as an energy source, our technology depended solely upon chemical combustion—specifically, the union of oxygen with a fossil fuel. This combustion, increasing daily as more people have demanded more power, has constituted the great "burnup" of the twentieth century.

A hundred years ago most of the nation's minute power needs were met by a renewable fuel, wood; but with the coming of the large steam boilers needed to produce electricity, the United States shifted to coal as its prime fuel.

A total of 37 billion tons of coal have been taken from the ground since 1900. The work force in the coal industry is now around one hundred thousand, but at its peak some six hundred thousand workers were employed in it. Stripmining increases worker productivity sharply, but the lack of regulation has allowed exploiters to dump the overburden of rock and earth (the spoil) without regard to the environment. About half of all U.S. coal is mined by stripping which, especially in hilly terrain, may result in polluted streams and massive earth scars.

Coal has had its ups and downs over the course of the century as other fuels have taken its place. At one time some

120 million tons of coal were used annually in coal-fired steam locomotives. These faded from the scene as the more efficient diesel-electric train came to dominate the nation's railways.

I remember the joy in our house when the family coal-burning stove was junked in favor of a gas stove. This was a particular delight for me because I was often assigned the chore of polishing the old coal stove with an atrocious black powder. Natural gas took over the job of heating our house, but not in time to save me from years of carrying coal in from the street, where it was dumped in a two-ton pile. Filling the family coal bin through a cellar window was an arduous fall and winter task that often fell to me as the youngest in the family.

What is coal's future? The data (Fig. 3-1) do not allow any reliable projection of future growth. But the U.S. Department of the Interior has estimated that 700 million tons of coal will be demanded by 1980 and that this will rise to 1 billion tons per year by the end of the century. This is not a spectacular growth, and the estimate is subject to many uncertainties. Even allowing for increased worker productivity, a larger miner force will be required to get a billion tons of coal out of the ground, especially if strip-mining is curtailed by federal regulation. If nuclear power fails to live up to its expectations, there may be an even greater demand for coal and a still larger mining force will be needed. Even if this does not happen, it is very probable that liquefaction of coal to produce oil and coal gasification will require increased coal production.

Coal, which was displaced because oil and natural gas were easier to transport and to use, could make a dramatic comeback if its conversion into oil or gas were to become economically feasible. At one time much of the gas used in U.S. cities was coal produced, so this is not really a startling innovation. As for converting coal into oil, Germany did it on an impressive scale during World War II, when it was cut off from its oil supply. Of course, normal economics did not prevail in wartime when the *Wehrmacht* had to have fuel, no matter what the cost, for tanks, trucks, ships, and planes. But in times of peace, the cheapest fuel is the one that is used, and oil from coal would not be countenanced in the United States unless it could meet the test of the marketplace. It is conceivable, however, that the U.S. government might subsidize coal liquefaction on national security grounds to prevent too great a dependence on foreign oil and its upsetting effect on the balance of payments.

Assuming that a commercially attractive means is developed for producing, say, two barrels of oil from a ton of coal, then 1 billion barrels of oil would require mining half a billion tons of coal. In Chapter 2 we saw that annual consumption of oil in the year 2000 might amount to a maximum of 15 billion barrels, of which perhaps a third might be obtained from the lower forty-eight states or offshore or Alaskan-Canadian sources. If 25 percent oil imports were allowed, oil synthesis from solid fuels would be called upon to provide over 6 billion barrels, requiring as much as 3 billion tons of coal. Added to the coal required for other purposes, a total of over 3 billion tons of coal would have to be extracted from the earth. Production on such a scale would create a tremendous problem for an industry customarily as harassed by labor strife as the coal industry is.

Could a different solid fuel be exploited to provide the needed oil—oil shale, for example? The United States has truly immense oil reserves locked up in shale deposits in a three-state area centered around Colorado. High-grade deposits, meaning 25 or more gallons of oil per ton of rock, extend over 17,000 square miles and contain an estimated 600 billion barrels of oil. About 80 percent of the U.S. oil shale is found beneath public lands, which come under the authority of the Department of the Interior. In 1971 President Nixon revived a long-dormant interest in oil-shale development by launching a prototype oil-shale leasing program. This is designed to create several prototype plants to produce a total of 200,000 barrels of oil per day. (The process involves heating the crushed shale at 900°F. to 1200°F. to release the oil.)

A yield of 25 gallons (roughly 0.6 barrels) per ton of oil shale means that producing 1 billion barrels of oil would require mining some 1.6 billion tons of rock. The ore would have to be processed near the excavation site and then disposed of. The spent ore is somewhat bulkier than the unprocessed shale, and to protect the environment, much of it might be returned to the original site. Presumably

FIGURE 3-1

COAL AND WOOD BURNING SINCE 1860

Wood exceeded coal as a source of heat until about 1885, at which time coal consumption soared. Between the end of World War I and the beginning of the Depression, coal consumption averaged 600 million tons a year. The yearly average for the past sixty years is about half a billion tons, or 13 quadrillion BTUs (QBTUs).* Actual coal production has zigzagged more from year to year than the line which is plotted for five-year intervals, would indicate.

* The Q here stands for quintillion, but it should be noted that resource specialists use the symbol Q, not combined with BTUs, as the energy unit for 1,000 quintillion BTUs.

FIGURE 3-1

COAL AND WOOD BURNING SINCE 1860

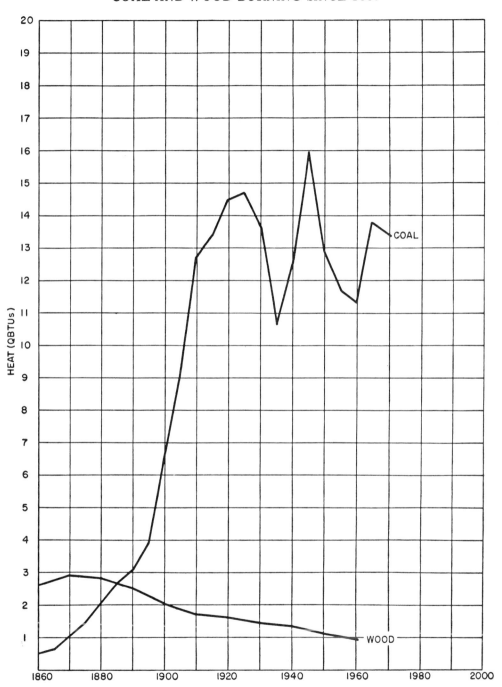

the rock would be mined chiefly by the room-and-pillar method which allows about three-fourths of the ore to be excavated. Overall, the threat to the environment seems less dire there than east of the Mississippi where coal strip-mining has caused its maximum depredation.

Reserves of oil shale appear ample to meet U.S. requirements, provided they can be tapped at a price of less than perhaps five dollars per barrel of product oil. It remains to be seen whether or not this goal can be attained. Compared with coal, the oil is low in sulfur and thus qualifies for commercial use. The high sulfur content of much coal east of the Mississippi rules it out for many utilities unless the sulfur can be reduced. Desulfuring coal is a major engineering problem, but once the coal is liquefied into oil, the sulfur can be removed in processing. This could be an important factor in the future use of coal.

In the meanwhile, any reckoning of the U.S. reserves of coal must take into account the sulfur content, rated low if under 1 percent, medium if between 1 and 3 percent, and high if over 3 percent. Deposits of all bituminous coal run to almost one-third of a trillion tons of all grades, with about 100 billion tons of low-sulfur coal and 90 billion tons of medium-grade known to exist. Most of the low-sulfur bituminous is west of the Mississippi, unfortunately remote from the big coal markets of the Northeast. The Montana-Dakota region has huge deposits of low-sulfur subbituminous and lignite—over 400 billion tons in all. Although it is prohibitively expensive to ship coal from Montana to the East, why would it not be possible in the future to build mine-mouth steam-electric plants fired by the coal, then feed the electricity into a national power grid? Provided, of course, that the mine-mouth plants conform to stringent standards set to maintain air quality and that the electricity is distributable.

A consortium known as WEST (Western Energy and Supply Transmission Associates), representing twenty-three energy companies in seven western states, has under construction a six-site program to produce a minimum of 14 million kilowatts, somewhat less than TVA, of electrical capacity. At full operating power these plants will burn up 47 million tons of coal per year. Much of the coal is mined on Indian land and transported as slurry by water pipes to the electric stations, which feed their output into power systems serving Los Angeles and other cities in the Southwest. California would not permit coal burning of the type used in the Four Corners plant near Fruitland, New Mexico, which has stirred up a storm of environmental opposition because of the fly ash emitted by its smokestacks and the impact of strip-mining and water used to transport coal and cool the plant condensers. As remote a coal-fired plant as this one is, then, is not exempt from ecological impact.

In appraising the fossil-fuel burnup of this century we covered oil in Chapter 2. Now we need to look at natural gas. Figuring gas consumption in the same QBTU units used for coal, we have plotted the epochal rise in use of this product— once so little valued that it was flared or burnt off at the wellhead. Before World War II the use of natural gas in America was not widespread; as may be seen in Figure 3-2, it fell far below coal and oil in the nation's energy accounts. However, the price advantage of a gas BTU as opposed to an oil BTU, and its inherent cleanliness, soon had their effect. By 1958 gas had overtaken coal as a source of energy.

Do we have enough natural gas to support such a growth rate in the future? The present estimate of the proved reserves in the lower forty-eight states and offshore as of January 1, 1970, is 275 Tcf; a high of 293 Tcf was reached in 1967, and since then production has exceeded additions to reserves. An actual production of 23 Tcf in 1971 places the reserve-to-production, or R/P, ratio at about 12:1, uncomfortably close to the 10:1 margin considered safe for energy-security purposes.

Although natural gas is extracted at an annual rate of one-tenth the total proved reserves, it does not mean that in ten years we will be out of gas. It does mean that the United States must find more gas in order to maintain the R/P ratio at a safe level. Here the discovery rate in the past few years has been very discouraging. At a time when gas is being consumed in ever-larger quantities, it is being found in smaller amounts; we are draining our reserves. For example, in 1970 a total 21.8 Tcf were produced while only 11.1 Tcf were added to reserves—a net decrease of 10.7 Tcf.

Looking further into the future, we may appreciate the urgency of the search even more. Future requirements total 1,160 Tcf for the next three decades. This means that if we

FIGURE 3-2

U.S. ENERGY SOURCES (1900–1970)
(Fossil Fuels)

The changing patterns of U.S. fossil-fuel consumption are evident when the use of all three is plotted on a BTU basis. Coal predominated until the mid-century, when oil became the prime fuel. In the 1960s natural gas also surpassed coal. In 1970 the total U.S. energy demand amounted to 68,810 trillion BTUs (68.8 QBTUs). It was supplied by the following fuel mix: oil, 43 percent; natural gas, 33 percent; coal, 20 percent; water power, 4 percent; nuclear power, 0.3 percent. If coal alone had been used, more than 2.5 billion tons would have been burned in 1970.

FIGURE 3-2

U.S. ENERGY SOURCES (1900–1970)
(Fossil Fuels)

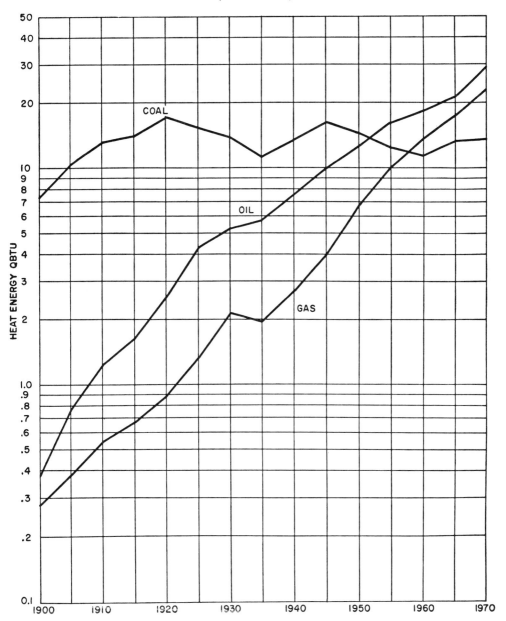

are to retain a proved reserve of as much as 500 Tcf in the year 2000, we must somehow find 1,500 Tcf of gas before the century ends.

In Figure 3-3, future demand has been projected on the basis of government estimates, but it is clear that this is a supply-moderated demand projection. Were utilities and industrial plants to be assured that they could get natural gas at reasonable prices, demand would skyrocket and would proceed along a line representing a continuation of the

FIGURE 3-3

U.S. CONSUMPTION OF NATURAL GAS

Projected consumption of natural gas through the next three decades is indicated by the dotted line. Any decline will be due to a shortage in supplies; the experts foresee no tapering off in demand. The total demand for the rest of the century amounts to 1,160 Tcf. Up to 1970, the U.S. had already used up 400 Tcf, or more than half the total amount discovered since exploration began.

FIGURE 3-3

U.S. CONSUMPTION OF NATURAL GAS

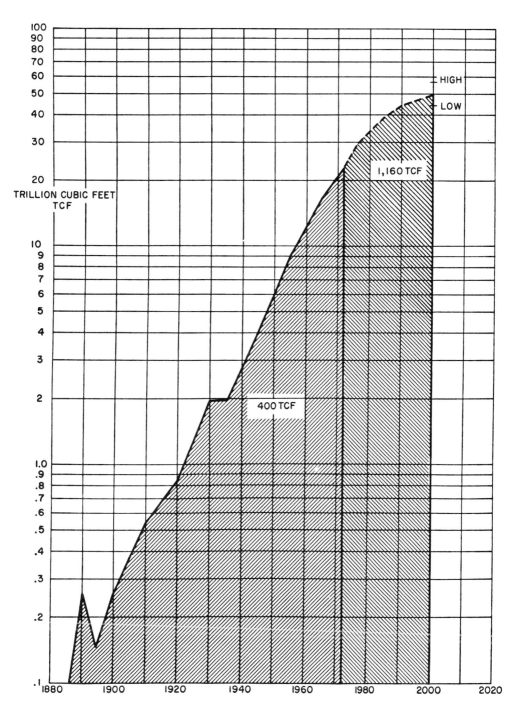

straight path of the past fifteen years. Such an arrow-flight course into the future would mean an annual consumption of about 110 Tcf in the year 2000. Thus the projection that has been made is a rather conservative one, being less than half that implied by the historic trend.

The United States has already burned up almost 400 Tcf of natural gas. If we add current proved reserves, this means we have discovered only about 700 Tcf in total since exploration began. How much more remains to be discovered? Not even the Federal Power Commission has access to the gas industry's data on reserves. In 1972, however, the FPC undertook a national survey which, while not really independent, has provided a more credible assessment of U.S. gas resources.

The U.S. energy expert, Dr. M. King Hubbert, estimates that the total potential supply for the lower forty-eight states and offshore is 690 Tcf, but less than half this volume is listed as "probable," most being classed as "possible" or "speculative." This is a gloomy forecast for the domestic gas supply, and it means that the provision of more gas to fill the future "gas gap" will become an increasingly urgent national necessity.

Alaskan gas may add significantly to the U.S. reserves, but a very long pipeline would be required to feed this gas into, say, the Chicago area. The longest U.S. pipeline, 36 inches in diameter, pumps about 1.5 billion cubic feet per day at maximum power. Larger-diameter pipelines could handle a trillion cubic feet per year. But multiple lines would still be needed for transporting enough gas to reduce shortages significantly.

Natural gas *can* be liquefied at very low temperatures (minus 258°F.) and shipped by special tankers, called floating Thermos jugs. Some Alaskan gas is processed in this way by Phillips Petroleum and Marathon Oil for shipment to Japan. These liquefied natural gas (LNG) exports amount to 50 billion cubic feet per year and are all handled by two Swedish-built tankers.

However, demand for natural gas is so great that significant quantities will be imported in LNG form and be city-gated, that is, piped to the city market on a wholesale basis at prices of $1.25 or more per Mcf (thousand cubic feet), which is double or triple the present city-gate price for many U.S. communities receiving their supplies from Texas and Louisiana fields. In fact, parts of the Midwest near Chicago will be receiving large quantities of gas taken from ocean wells off Trinidad, liquefied on the island, shipped by LNG tanker to Gulf ports, gasified, and then pumped northward to Indiana. LNG tankers capable of carrying 2 billion cubic feet or more will be employed in bringing foreign gas to U.S. ports. Like oil imports, LNG places reliance on the continuity of supply from a foreign nation (Russia may actually be a major source of LNG for the U.S.) and also serves to increase the trade deficit.

The synthesis of gas by "gasification" of coal is an option available to us, but such an artificial source must be cheap and must meet the test of environmental innocuousness. A number of prototype plants designed to produce 250 to 500 million cubic feet of gas per day are under way. The coal consumed in producing a trillion cubic feet of gas would probably run about 60 million tons, so that gasification of 600 million tons (total coal production for 1971) would be required to supply only 20 percent of the year-2000 demand. If only so much coal can be mined, then a system of priorities will probably have to be applied, defining coal use as solid or liquid or gaseous.

Synthesis of gas from solid fuels will take time, and it by no means promises to meet the fuel crises even of the seventies. Furthermore, very large capital outlays will have to be made to construct synthesis plants capable of providing liquid or gaseous fuel at a rate that will fill a sizable part of the total demand. If the primary determinant in the use of coal were to be the maximization of profit, and not the most efficient use of fuel, then private enterprise and the public interest might be in basic conflict.

The past century of energy use in the United States is represented in Figure 3-4 where total energy has been expressed in BTUs. If one adjusts for the setbacks of the Depression years, then the sequence of points on the energy curve conforms to a fairly straight line from the year 1900 to the year 1972.

The extrapolation over a thirty-year period, based on a century of historic data, does not afford much leeway when the growth rate conforms to a 3 percent annual increase. Even

FIGURE 3-4

U.S. TOTAL ENERGY CONSUMPTION

Projections by the U.S. Department of the Interior of energy consumption for the rest of the century (dotted line) follow the pattern of the preceding postwar period. The department anticipates a doubling of energy demand every quarter-century, or a continuation of a 3 percent annual increase, the past century's average. The rate of increase seems modest in the short run, but in the span of a century it means a fiftyfold expansion. The population increase counts for only a small part of the increase in energy usage, known and projected. By the end of the century, per capita usage is expected to be six times as much as it was when the century began. The total burnup for the hundred years will be the equivalent of about a trillion barrels of oil.

FIGURE 3-4

U.S. TOTAL ENERGY CONSUMPTION

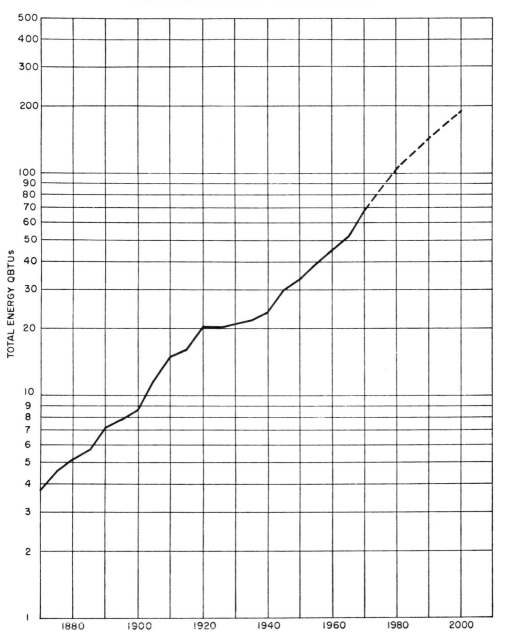

if energy growth does slacken, it is unlikely to drop much below, say, 170 quintillion BTUs for the year 2000. In either case
the United States can no longer assume that more and more
fuel will be available simply as a matter of course.

Figure 3-5 illustrates how the per capita consumption of
energy has changed from 1900 to the present and how future
demands may increase this value. One reason why the curve
rises so sharply toward the end of the century is that the
energy forms will feature electricity. Since the fuel-to-energy

FIGURE 3-5

INDIVIDUAL ENERGY CONSUMPTION
(1870–2000)

In 1900 the average American used energy at the rate
of 113 million BTUs a year, roughly equivalent to 20
barrels of petroleum. By 1970 the per capita use had
tripled. By the end of the century it is expected to soar to
the equivalent of more than 11 barrels of oil a year
per person. For the whole country that would mean using
as much energy in one year as could be generated by
more than 30 billion barrels of oil. The future projection
(dotted line) is based on estimates made by the U.S.
Department of the Interior.

FIGURE 3-5

INDIVIDUAL ENERGY CONSUMPTION
(1870–2000)

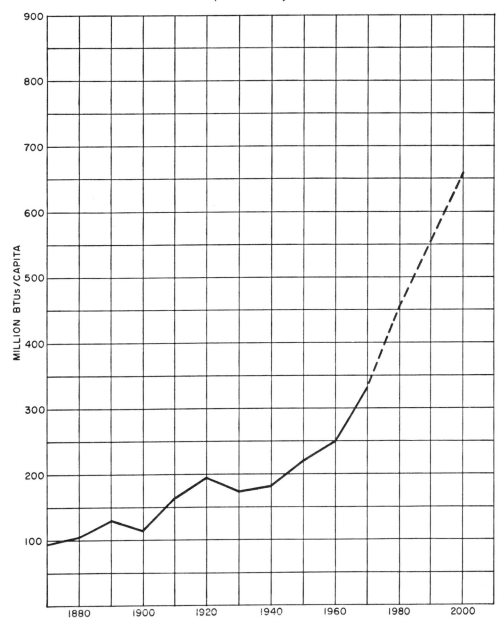

conversion in steam-electric plants has at best only 40 percent efficiency, and since substitution of electric energy for heating purposes is energy wasteful, the energy usage will increase. The curve also reflects the greater saturation of energy markets as more people purchase energy-consuming goods. Thus it is the combination of per capita consumption and population increase which accounts for the total increase in energy used, the former being a sevenfold increase and the latter a tripling over the course of the century.

It is clear that U.S. demands for natural gas must slacken, because they cannot possibly be met if they continue on their historic line. It is also hard to believe that U.S. miners will dig coal out of the ground at a rate exceeding 1 billion tons by the year 2000, although an energy crisis might make it necessary. Since the amounts of coal and gas add up to about 7 QBTUs, and the total energy consumption for the year 2000 is estimated at 190 QBTUs, this leaves 120 QBTUs to be supplied from other sources. Hydropower will probably supply less than 3 percent of the total, leaving about 115 QBTUs to come from oil. But that means 20 billion barrels— an amount that staggers the imagination of even the most optimistic oilman.

In midsummer of 1971, Interior Secretary Rogers C. B. Morton testified before a Senate committee that oil is expected to supply 66 QBTUs of energy in the year 2000. Subtracting this from our total of 115 QBTUs leaves almost 50 QBTUs, to be supplied from some new source. In a word, *uranium.* Nuclear power is being counted on to fill the energy gap in the year 2000. In fact, the top planners in government are banking on the uranium atom to provide a major part of U.S. electric energy in the future. Figure 3-6 shows the growth of electric energy from 1900 to 1970 with two extrapolations to the year 2000. In this illustration we have plotted the growth of electric-power capacity, that is, the ability to produce electricity, as measured in millions of kilowatts. We shall also be using the term *megawatt,* which is a thousand kilowatts. Energy, as already noted, is measured in the product of power multiplied by time, that is, kilowatt-hours. We may now examine the resources needed.

The introduction of electricity into the metropolitan environment was not without its birth pains. Before the turn of the century, when George Westinghouse proposed bringing alternating current into Manhattan to replace the low-voltage direct current then installed, he met some violent reaction. People feared that electricity would leak from transformers and invade their homes. Thomas Edison worried about the reliability of insulation against electricity above a 200-volt level. (Today voltages a thousandfold higher are carried underground.) Now cities are paralyzed if they do not receive a constant flow of electricity, and a power blackout for any length of time imposes severe stress on any community. Factories shut down, television screens are darkened, hospitals are forced to switch to emergency power, people are stranded in high-rise buildings, transportation falters, food defrosts in deep freezers, radios are silenced, and many homes go unheated or lose their air-conditioned comfort. I was once marooned on Martha's Vineyard during a hurricane. It seemed that everything in the house where I was staying depended on electrical power—even the toilets would not work, because the water pump was powerless; automobiles were idled because the electric gas pumps could not be used.

America is switching to electric energy at a rate that challenges the capacity of the nation's utilities.

Coal has been the primary utility fuel throughout the century, and in 1970 central stations purchased 62 percent of all the coal consumed in the United States. It provided 46 percent of all electricity generated in that year, while natural gas accounted for 24 percent, and oil about 12 percent. Hydropower produced 16 percent, and nuclear power slightly more than 1 percent. All in all, the oil equivalent of the 17 QBTUs of energy involved in generating this 1.5 trillion kilowatt-hours of electricity amounted to almost 3 billion barrels. (For the sake of completeness, it is necessary to note that almost all electric energy produced in the

United States is of public-utility generation. Industrial plants generate about 7 percent of the utility total for their own consumption.)

Since the nation's total fuel burnup in 1970 amounted to 68 QBTUs and that used in electric generation is 17 QBTUs, the United States was then 25 percent electrified. At mid-century only a tenth of the nation's energy was electrical, but in another third of a century the proportion will be a half. This electrification of the nation will necessarily concentrate energy production in a few geographic sites where

FIGURE 3-6

U.S. ELECTRIC GENERATING CAPACITY
(1900–2000)

The top line represents the growth in the capacity of the nation's electric-power units. On an average, each kilowatt of installed capacity turns out 5,000 kilowatt-hours. In the early part of the century, the figure was much lower. Inefficient coal-fired steam generators, burning seven or more pounds of coal for each kilowatt-hour produced, and low-power, water-driven generators were gradually displaced. Units reached a 200,000-kilowatt rating in 1929. In the 1960s the million-kilowatt generating unit was ushered in, along with a new unit of measure, the megawatt (Mw), which is 1 million watts, or 1,000 kilowatts. Projections of utility-energy sources (the dotted extensions of the three lower lines) anticipate the predominance of nuclear-power units before the end of the century. If the projection of the total (top line) is valid, electric-power capacity will henceforth be doubling every twelve years.

FIGURE 3-6

U.S. ELECTRIC GENERATING CAPACITY
(1900–2000)

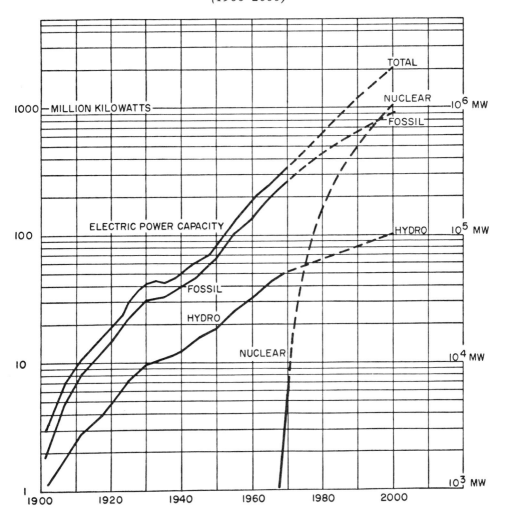

very large quantities of energy will be released. The resulting environmental hazards must be minimized by long-range planning on the part of the federal government, the utilities, and the local area. The data presented in Figure 3-6 show that the energy sources supplying the generation of this electric power are scheduled to undergo a dramatic change in the future. Hydropower will continue to grow, but very slowly, constituting only about a twentieth of the U.S. electric capacity in the year 2000. Fossil-fueled plants will triple in capacity, so that by the century's end they will be consuming the equivalent of almost 900 million tons of coal per year.

It is not possible to predict the fossil-fuel mix that steam plants will be supplied. It does seem evident that the premium fuels—oil and natural gas—will be tightly rationed for utility consumption. For example, a Federal Power Commission power survey for California estimated that 0.64 Tcf of natural gas were consumed in 1970 by electric utilities and that 30 percent less gas would be available for power generation in California by 1990. If gas synthesis from coal proves economically attractive and environmentally tolerable, this fuel mix might change. On the other hand, if mine-mouth plants using solid coal or lignite were coupled to a national electric power grid, then coal could still dominate the fossil-fuel feed to the electric utilities.

Our projection of the electric future assumes that nuclear power will overtake fossil fuels as the mainstay of the utilities, probably by about 1995. Our next chapter will consider nuclear technology in detail.

Will the U.S. electric-energy consumption continue to escalate after the year 2000? Making a forecast of energy in the twenty-first century is like fortune-telling with tea leaves —in the age of the tea bag—but I have made a fearless forecast of the next century of U.S. electric-energy consumption (Fig. 3-7). I make the assumption that the electric-energy curve will undergo a marked bending over as it penetrates the twenty-first century. In drawing this projection, I assume two things: first, that electric energy will lose momentum in usurping a larger percentage of the total energy market. There are many end uses for energy where electricity loses out to competing forms for a variety of reasons, some technical and some economic. I anticipate that some limits will be imposed on the use of electricity for space heating. When a home is heated with oil or natural gas, heat is directly produced and utilized as such on the spot, usually with an efficiency of 60 percent or so. However, electric heating involves burning some fuel at a central station with about 40 percent efficiency, converting it to electricity, and then transmitting the electricity to the home where it is converted back into heat. In practice, it turns out that home builders often sacrifice efficiency in installation of gas heaters, so that electric heating is not as energy wasteful as the relative efficiencies would indicate. Nonetheless, the theoretical comparison reflects the waste potential of an all-electric home or building. Should the supply of natural gas be curtailed, then builders would have no option but to install electric heating or compel buyers to accept oil heating. Second, I assume that the per capita consumption of electric energy will tend to reach a saturation value, that is, that the sharply ascendant curve in Figure 3-5 will in the future bend over and will tend to flatten out by the middle of the twenty-first century. (See Chapter 7.)

Obviously, any projection of future energy demands must take population growth into account. It took the United States slightly more than half a century to grow from 100 million to 200 million in population, and, with that doubling time, it would reach 400 million in 2020. (I optimistically assume that this level of population will not be reached until after the mid-century.) In any event the historic growth curve of electric energy must bend over, shifting from its post-1950 doubling time of about one decade to several decades after the start of the next century, and then lengthening even more thereafter. A "steady-state" consumption of 20 trillion kilowatt-hours of electric energy hereafter does not necessarily mean a zero population growth in the year 2070. I would expect that after the year 2000, the use of premium fossil fuels or coal-synthesized fuel for transportation would decline as the family car or personal vehicle yielded to mass-transit systems.

The annual production of 20 trillion kilowatt-hours of electric energy would consume over 30 billion barrels of petroleum or its fossil-fuel equivalent. Even if all the sulfur oxide and other pollutants could be strictly controlled, there

FIGURE 3-7

ELECTRIC ENERGY: THIS CENTURY AND THE NEXT

A long-range forecast of the U.S. use of electric energy assumes a bending over of the curve after the year 2000 due to market saturation and to a reduction in the rate of the population increase. Even on this bent-over projection the strain on the U.S. energy industry will be extreme since by the turn of the century about a thousand electric plants of 1,000 megawatt power will have to be built in a decade to replace old plants and to add new generating capacity. Thereafter as the growth curve flattens out the replacement market for power plants will begin to resemble that of the automobile. Industry will be building units to replace obsolete plants more than to add new capacity.

It is interesting to note that cigarette consumption (Fig. 1-6) can be plotted on this same scale. It turns out that the cigarette curve from 1920 to midcentury closely fits the electric energy consumption and 1 kilowatt-hour "equals" one cigarette smoked. The correlation is fortuitous. If one were to extrapolate cigarette smoking along the above curve for electric energy, then by the year 2000 the average American smoker would be puffing 14 packs per day. Obviously there are limits to extrapolation.

FIGURE 3-7

ELECTRIC ENERGY: THIS CENTURY
AND THE NEXT

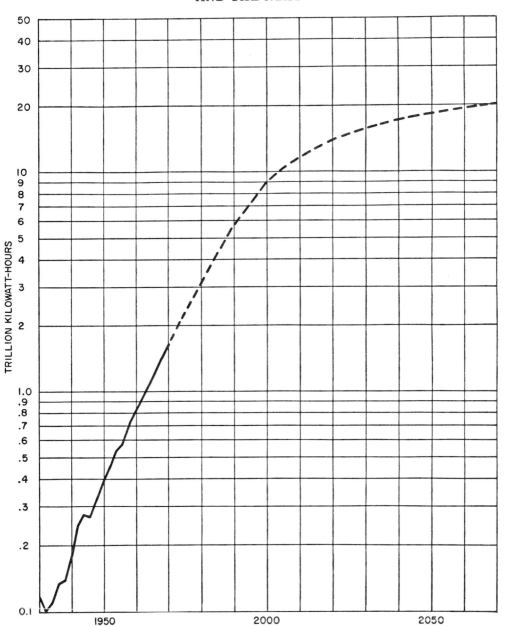

would be the inevitable release of carbon dioxide to the atmosphere.

Scientists have become increasingly concerned about the climatological effects of high concentrations of carbon dioxide in the atmosphere; they foresee a "greenhouse effect" that would cause the earth to become warmer. A temperature increase of only 2°F. to 3°F. could, as the first annual report of the U.S. Council on Environmental Quality warned, "in a period of a few decades, lead to the start of substantial melting of the ice caps and flooding of coastal regions." The warming effect of an increase of carbon dioxide in the atmosphere still has to be researched thoroughly, but it is a serious enough threat to have been included in the first report of the nation's highest environmental authority.

In certain geographic areas where the meteorological conditions tend to stagnate air in a natural basin, as in Los Angeles, the 4 percent annual growth in energy consumption can have a thermal effect in causing ambient air temperatures to rise significantly. For example, E. J. List of the California Institute of Technology's Environmental Quality Laboratory has estimated that 94 percent of the state's energy is derived from fossil fuels and that in twenty years continued energy consumption "would add temperature increments of 5–7° F. on days of poor natural ventilation."

The resource drain on fossil-fuel reserves and the environmental impact of extracting them is of serious concern and is a prime reason for the U.S. decision to "go nuclear" and exploit the energy locked in the uranium atom.

CHAPTER

4

THE GROWTH OF NUCLEAR POWER

In the August 3, 1935, issue of *Nature,* a British scientific journal, there was an article titled "Isotopic Constitution of Uranium" by a Canadian-born physicist, Arthur J. Dempster. Working in his first-floor laboratory on the University of Chicago campus, behind black curtains that screened off a view of the tennis courts outside, the slightly built physicist had sparked a tiny piece of uranium in the vacuum of his atom-weighing device. He had only wanted to see if, possibly, uranium had atoms of different weight. Other experimenters had found it to be composed of a single-weight atom, or isotope, of 238 mass units—hence, the symbol U (for uranium) 238.

Dempster's special weighing machine bent a beam of uranium atoms, first with an electrical field and then with a powerful magnetic field, so that they focused on a photographic plate containing a sensitive emulsion. He readily identified the abundant isotope U-238, but he saw "in addition, on long exposures, a faint companion of atomic weight 235." He estimated that less than 1 percent of uranium consisted of the U-235 atoms.

At the time I was still in high school and unaware of the significance of the discovery. Five years later I was a student of Dr. Dempster's, and I learned that he himself attached no particular importance to it. Yet when the uranium atom was split by two German chemists late in 1938, it was the scarce "companion" form of uranium that split, and not the abundant U-238. The whole evolution of atomic energy was to be based on this single form of uranium, which, as later research showed, formed only 0.7 percent of uranium itself.

The splitting or fission of a uranium atom releases much more energy than a chemical process, such as the combustion of coal. The energy let loose in a single combination of carbon and oxygen amounts to 4 electron-volts—to use the unit of energy that nuclear experts prefer. An electron-volt is the energy gained by an electron in passing through a potential difference of one volt; it is an extremely small tidbit of energy. But a pound of carbon, or coal, contains an immense number of tidbits. In fission, which we will call "nuclear burning," even though no flame occurs, a single atom of uranium releases 200 million electron-volts of energy. This means that, atom for atom, fission is 50 million times as potent as burning.

Before we jump to the conclusion that we can forget about coal (assuming nuclear power is available), we need to look more closely at some other numbers. First, on a pound-for-pound basis, it turns out that there are twenty times as many atoms in carbon as in uranium; this reduces the energy advantage of uranium over coal to 2.5 million to 1. Thus, one pound of uranium is equal to 2.5 million pounds, or 1,250 tons, of coal. Second, on a dollar-for-dollar fuel basis, uranium is very expensive, running ten dollars per pound for pure metal, or four thousand times as much as coal. This consideration shrinks the uranium-to-coal advantage to 625 to 1. Third, if it is only the U-235 content of one pound of uranium that can be tapped, we must divide 625 by 139, which is the ratio of the U-238 to the U-235 atoms. This final shrinkage reduces the nuclear advantage to 4.5 to 1.

Even a factor of 4.5 is an incentive to a utility, since

it would mean using fuel at a cost that compares with about one dollar for a ton of coal. However, this digression into nuclear economics has glossed over a number of critical points.

For one thing, it has been assumed that the capital costs for a nuclear plant are the same as for a conventional coal-fired unit. But a number of requirements add to the cost of a nuclear steam boiler and thus tend to tip the scales in favor of coal or some other fossil fuel.

Then there is the fact that ten dollars does not cover the full cost of a pound of nuclear fuel. The uranium has to be especially processed, as we shall shortly see, and this adds to the nuclear costs. In addition, we have assumed that *all* U-235 atoms would be fissioned in a nuclear power unit, in a complete nuclear burnup. In practice, this is not possible and, again, the nuclear advantage of uranium fuel shrinks.

All these facts were well-known in 1939, at a time when a successful chain reaction in uranium was very much in doubt —in fact, a friend of mine, Dr. Richard B. Roberts of the Carnegie Institution in Washington, D.C., and a colleague of his published a paper, "Uranium and Atomic Power," in the September 1939 issue of the *Journal of Applied Physics,* making an analysis like the one I have made here.

Before World War II, scientists who recognized the great military potential of atomic energy voluntarily imposed secrecy to keep their experimental results on nuclear fission from reaching Germany, and they took the initiative in urging President Roosevelt to foster development of the atomic bomb. Because U-235 was pinpointed as the prime weapon material, the next step was to separate it from natural uranium, ridding it of its heavy companion U-238. Since both atoms belong to the same element, they are chemical kin and cannot, so to speak, be separated in a test tube. The techniques of the physicist, which would differentiate the two atoms by the slight difference in weight, had to be applied to effect a separation.

A variety of separation techniques appeared promising,

but, as it turned out, the gaseous-diffusion method became the favored one here. In this method, uranium metal, a silvery, heavier-than-lead element, is converted into uranium hexafluoride, a greenish, highly toxic gas, which serves as the feed material for a gaseous-diffusion plant. Then the gas is pumped into the first of the 2,304 stages of a huge continuous-flow pipeline. The wartime plant, built at Oak Ridge, Tennessee, cost $347 million and covered 40 acres. At each stage the uranium gas was pumped against a porous barrier or membrane through which the U-235 atoms, being lighter, diffused at a slightly faster rate than the more abundant heavy U-238 atoms. Recycling the gas through stage after stage yielded a product concentrated or enriched in U-235. Weapon-grade material, containing more than 90 percent U-235, was the objective of the Oak Ridge development.

In the early days of the A-bomb project, we were not sure that the Oak Ridge process would pay off in time, so a quite different approach to making bombstuff was undertaken—the so-called plutonium route. This bold attempt to deliberately manufacture in quantity an element just as explosive as U-235, yet unknown to man and unavailable in nature, was a result of basic research in which scientists discovered the new element by bombarding uranium with neutrons. (Neutrons are elementary nuclear particles, electrically neutral and as heavy as a hydrogen atom, which are given off when a uranium atom is fissioned.) Uranium is the last of ninety-two elements in the periodic system, whereas plutonium is element 94. An intermediate element 93 (neptunium) is the atom from which plutonium is born. To make plutonium it was necessary to provide a continuous and concentrated source of neutrons, that is, a chain reaction, in uranium.

The first successful chain reaction was achieved on December 2, 1942, at Stagg Field on the University of Chicago campus. I have always found it intriguing that Dr. Dempster made his discovery of U-235 in a room only a dozen paces from a tennis court and that the first chain reaction took place in a nearby squash court under the football-stadium stands. My own research had a somewhat elevated position; I completed my doctoral work in the press box atop the Stagg Field Stadium, where I had room to spread out an array of Geiger counters and electronic devices to track down the origin of certain cosmic rays. But even before my research was finished, I found myself working half time on the A-bomb project as Dr. Dempster's first assistant. Tackling nuclear fission was something of a comedown for me, at least energywise; my research had concentrated on really high energy particles, some of which exceeded a billion trillion electron-volts.

The Stagg Field chain reaction was a proof-of-principle experiment involving an assembly of many tons of graphite interspersed in a regular and carefully calculated manner with lumps of uranium. Neither the uranium nor the graphite was very pure, but the assembly did sustain a very weak, or low-power, chain reaction, paving the way for the design of much more powerful assemblies, or "piles," as they were called in those days. (Now we call them nuclear reactors.) Being of such low power—not potent enough to run a television set if its power could have been tapped—the Stagg Field reactor needed no cooling. However, units powerful enough to produce plutonium in useful quantities, about half a pound per day, would inevitably give off so much heat that cooling then became a problem. The plutonium production reactors, a total of three, were built on the banks of the Columbia River in the state of Washington, where plenty of cold water was available.

During the war, removing the heat from a reactor to keep its core from deteriorating or even melting was an expensive nuisance, but all of us who worked on the project could see the virtues of this waste heat for peacetime. Once the war was over, reactors could be designed specifically to produce heat—to make steam to make electric power. In this way, a nuclear core would substitute for the firebox of a coal-fired boiler.

Both methods of producing bomb material paid off in 1945,

and by midsummer bombs were assembled and used as military weapons. The first A-bomb dropped on Japan drew its energy from U-235 and exploded with a power of 13,000 tons of TNT, equivalent to 13 kilotons. A plutonium weapon of improved design, dropped over Nagasaki, detonated with a yield of 21 kilotons. Peacetime brought no letup in the atomic arms race as the United States and the Soviet Union engaged in a nuclear competition (Fig. 4-1).

The most powerful H-bomb, a 58-megaton weapon, was

FIGURE 4-1

THE GROWTH OF WEAPON POWER

The sevenfold logarithmic scale of weapon explosiveness begins with the largest conventional high explosive of World War II, a ten-ton blockbuster, and jumps abruptly to the Hiroshima A-bomb. Then there is a period of transition during which more powerful A-bombs are developed, culminating in the development of H-bombs. A-bomb power can be stated in kilotons, but "megaton"—equivalent to 1 million tons of TNT—was needed to refer to the explosive power of hydrogen weapons.

FIGURE 4-1

THE GROWTH OF WEAPON POWER

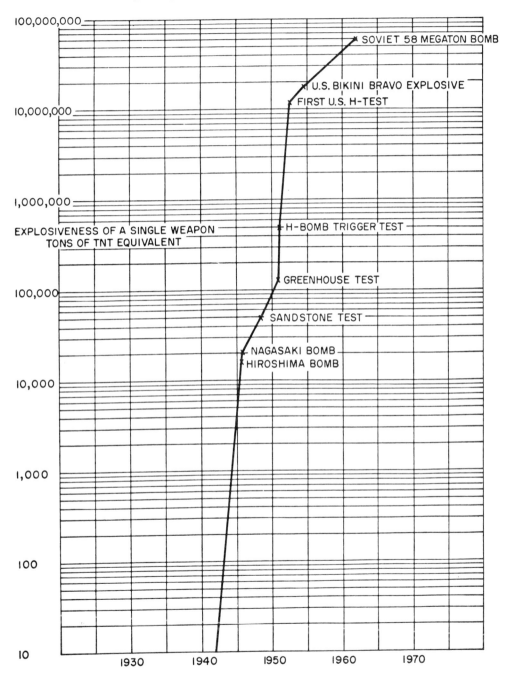

detonated in October 1961 by the Soviet Union. Actually, the explosiveness of this bomb would have exceeded 100 megatons had it been rigged to exploit the energy boost of an outer jacket of ordinary uranium. But it was not so rigged, presumably because the Soviet weapons experts feared the worldwide reaction to the radioactive contamination that would have resulted. The 100 million increase in a single weapon's explosiveness within a period of two decades must surely represent the ultimate in logarithmic growth. No other curve in this book illustrates such a dramatic rise. It literally splits historic time asunder, dividing it into two eras—pre-atomic and atomic. And the portentousness of this great bisector of human history is as great in fact as it appears to be on a graph.

The radioactivity associated with nuclear weapons, and with nuclear-power production as well, constitutes a unique hazard to man, one not demonstrable on a logarithmic chart. A purely statistical approach fails when one confronts an innovation that is different in kind from anything man has experienced in his struggle to survive. For example, as a result of a single bomb test in the remote Pacific, every living person born in the United States has in his bones measurable quantities of strontium 90, a radioactive species uniquely produced in a nuclear explosion.

To return to the development of the peacetime uses of nuclear energy, I recall that when the war ended many physicists were confident that taming the chain reaction for the production of electric power would be a straightforward process—merely a matter of engineering certain reactors to produce steam to turn the blades of a turbogenerator. Scientists began a crusade to divorce the atom from military control and, partly as a result of their efforts, a civilian agency —the Atomic Energy Commission (AEC)—was created by an act of Congress.

The wartime success of the Hanford reactors in producing plutonium seemed to be a good technical base for launching a program of nuclear-power development. After all, the reactors did produce 250,000 kilowatts of heat, and they ran very smoothly. However, converting such devices to generators of high-temperature steam proved to be a tough technical undertaking. Things might have gone faster had the AEC not attached such a high priority to continued development of nuclear weapons. One cannot look back on the postwar days of the AEC as a time of vigorous research on civilian power. In fact, in the power field, the AEC took a military detour, bowing before the Navy's demands for a nuclear-propulsion reactor for submarine application. (Perhaps one should substitute "Admiral Rickover's" for "the Navy's" in the preceding sentence, since that officer was the driving force in the nuclear-submarine effort.)

Water reactors had been settled on as the best bet for underwater propulsion. As a result, certain technologies useful for this type of reactor were developed; for example, it was essential to encapsulate uranium fuel in a corrosion-resistant cladding, and Rickover pushed hard for a zirconium alloy (zircaloy) to fill the bill. But naval reactors are rather low in power, about 70,000 thermal kilowatts, while to keep pace with fossil-fuel units commercial nuclear plants would have to be 2 to 4 million kilowatts in thermal-power rating. Thus there was a considerable gap to be vaulted in moving from naval to commercial nuclear technology.

The utilities relied upon the AEC and industrial companies to develop the prototypes of commercial plants, and the AEC committed a total of about $2 billion to the enterprise. Yet it was not until the late sixties that the utilities began to bring plants on stream; they could scarcely make the decision to go nuclear, especially in view of higher capital costs, until they felt sure that uranium promised to compete economically with fossil fuel. The turning point for the utilities came in the mid-sixties when General Electric, a prime manufacturer of nuclear steam units, looked over the costs of the Oyster Creek plant it had designed for New Jersey Central Power and Light Company and decided that the economics of nuclear power were favorable. During the 1969–71 period, power companies had difficulty in getting an adequate supply of certain fossil fuels in the face of rising prices. Many utilities were persuaded by the high cost of coal and by their inability to switch to an assured source of natural gas or residual oil that their best bet was to order more nuclear units.

Of course the most densely populated states took the lead. As of 1972, six states had the following nuclear-electric-power capacity complete, under construction, or on order for completion by 1980:

1. Illinois	12,056	megawatts
2. Pennsylvania	11,800	
3. California	8,500	
4. New Jersey	8,400	
5. New York	7,830	
6. North Carolina	6,602	
Total	55,188	megawatts

A total of 30 reactors operating in 1973 has almost 13,000 megawatts of electric capacity, while twice as many are under construction, with a total of three times as much capacity, and an almost equal number of reactors are on order for construction in the next decade, bringing the total to about 150 reactors, scheduled to produce over 125,000 megawatts of power. However, additional growth was projected by the AEC to bring the 1980 nuclear-electric capacity to 150,000 megawatts (Fig. 4-2).

A number of factors have combined to delay construction of nuclear plants, one of them being delays in the regulatory process which comes under the jurisdiction of the Atomic Energy Commission.

The AEC has a dual authority with respect to nuclear reactors; under the terms of the Atomic Energy Act, it is charged both with promoting and developing nuclear power and with the responsibility for regulating the nuclear-power industry. Critics of the AEC have charged that this dual role results in a conflict of interest. Utilities, on the other hand, complain that the AEC's regulatory arm is excessively restrictive in issuing construction permits and operating licenses for commercial power plants.

My own view is that the siting of nuclear-power plants should be subject to the strictest control so that, in the event of an accident, no major population sector would be exposed to potentially harmful radioactivity. I admit that nuclear accidents are low in probability, but they are potentially high in consequence. This fact must be taken into account not only in the basic design and construction of the plant and the supervision of its operation but also in selecting a site whose potential fallout shadow does not penumbrate a large population.

A nuclear-reactor core is quite different from the firebox of a conventional steam plant. Powdered coal, natural gas, or residual oil is introduced into the combustion chamber of a firebox at a controlled rate, usually about 200 pounds per second for a large fossil-fuel installation. Should a steam pipe in the boiler break, there is an automatic shutdown of the fuel injection, and the residual heat in the firebox does not pose a safety problem for the community outside the plant fence. In a nuclear reactor, the core is a cylindrical volume about 12 feet high and 11 feet wide, consisting of half a million pounds of material. The uranium fuel, usually enriched so as to be 3 percent or so in U-235 content, is prepared in the form of small pellets or cylinders, each weighing little more than a third of an ounce. These pellets are stacked to form a 12-foot-long rod which is sheathed in a zircaloy tube; then bundles of these fuel rods are arranged in a structure known as a fuel assembly. In a representative reactor core, there might be close to 200 fuel assemblies, each holding 204 fuel rods. Each bundle of fuel rods is fixed in the reactor core so that water under pressure flows around it and removes the heat of fission. All in all, a typical pressurized water-reactor core might contain 10 million uranium dioxide fuel pellets weighing about 200,000 pounds. The core also contains movable rods, called control rods, which are designed to slide in and out of the core. An element such as cadmium, boron, or silver absorbs neutrons, and when made part of the control rod, can raise or lower the amount of power generated in the core.

Along the center line of each uranium pellet, the temperature rises to about 4,100°F. when the reactor operates at full power. Heat from the pellet flows outward to the zircaloy jacket, where it is transferred to the water coolant. In

FIGURE 4-2

U.S. NUCLEAR POWER GROWTH

Some idea of the growth pattern inherent in the country's nuclear power planning can be gained from this chart. The incremental growth of nuclear power is detailed on a time scale, according to the year a new plant comes into production. The power plants identified by power rating and name are positioned on the chart in the time frame at which they are expected to become operational. Because of delays in construction and licensing, these dates may not be met as anticipated on the chart.

FIGURE 4-2

U.S. NUCLEAR POWER GROWTH

US NUCLEAR POWER GROWTH
REACTORS USING ENRICHED FUEL

Operating, Ordered and Announced
For Commercial Operation
Current as of Dec. 31, 1971
Prepared by Operational Planning & Power Div.,
Oak Ridge Operations
U. S. Atomic Energy Commission

NOTE: The installed capacity is the sum
of the ultimate capacities as projected by the utilities.

INSTALLED CAPACITY - MWe X 10³

CALENDAR YEARS

122,631
117,626
111,206
98,580
82,930
66,073
61,998
50,696
36,064
20,175
7,812

915 Virgil C. Summer-2 (South Car. E&G)
1160 HTGR-2 (Phil.Elect.) HTGR
900 Rome Point No. 2 (New Eng.Elect.) PWR
1150 Quanicassee-2 (Consumers Pwr.)
880 Perry-1 (Cleve. Elect. Illum.)
1100 Union Electric-1 (Union Elect.)
1120 Susquehanna-2 (Penna. P&L) BWR
1250 Mid-South-2 (Miss. P&L)
1150 Quanicassee-1 (Consumers Pwr.)
900 Shearon Harris-4 (Car. P&L) PWR
900 Perryman-2 (Balt.G&E)
1088 Newbold Island-2 (Pub.Serv.E&G)BWR

1180 HTGR-1 (Phil.Elect.) HTGR
1128 Mendocino-2 (PG&E) BWR
900 Rome Point No. 1 (New Eng.Elect.)
1250 Mid-South-1 (Miss. P&L)
1100 Tulare County-2 (L.A.Dept.W&P)
900 River Bend Station (GUSU)
1100 Alvin W. Vogtle No. 2 (Ga.Pwr.) PWR
1100 Delmarva-1 (Delmarva P&L) HTGR
1100 Com.Ed.-2 (Com.Ed.) PWR
900 Shearon Harris-3 (Car.P&L) PWR

900 Perryman-1 (Balt.G&E)
1100 Alvin W. Vogtle No. 1 (Ga.Pwr.)
940 North Anna-4 (VEPCO) PWR
1279 TVA-9 (TVA) PWR
1140 San Onofre-3 (So.Cal.Ed./San Diego G&E)
1088 Newbold Island-1 (Pub.Serv.E&G) BWR
1120 Susquehanna-1 (Penna.P&L)
1128 Mendocino-1 (PG&E) BWR
1100 Tulare County-1 (L.A.Dept. Water & Pwr.)
892 Crystal River-4 (Fla.Pwr.) PWR
847 Beaver Valley-2 (Duquesne Light) PWR
818 Midland-2 (Consumers Pwr.)
1115 Verplanck Unit 1 (Con.Ed.)
1100 Com.Ed.-1 (Com.Ed.) PWR
1078 LaSalle Co. Nuclear-2 (Com.Ed.) BWR
900 Shearon Harris-2 (Car.P&L) PWR

1103 Hanford-2 (WPPSS) BWR
940 North Anna-3 (VEPCO) PWR
1279 TVA-8 (TVA) PWR
1230 Watts Bar-2 (TVA) PWR
1140 San Onofre-2 (So.Cal.Ed./San Diego G&E) PWR
915 Virgil C. Summer-1 (So.Car.E&G) PWR
1100 Limerick-2 (Phil.Elect.) BWR
1100 Nine Mile Point-2 (Niagara Mohawk) BWR
1165 Waterford-3 (La. P&L) PWR
854 Shoreham (Long Is. Light.) BWR
1205 Forked River-1 (Jersey Cen.P&L) PWR
1150 William B. McGuire-2 (Duke Pwr.) PWR
800 Midland-1 (Consumers Pwr.) PWR
1078 LaSalle Co. Nuclear-1 (Com.Ed.) BWR
900 Shearon Harris-1 (Car. P&L) PWR
898 Joseph M. Farley-2 (Ala.Pwr.) PWR
1219 Watts Bar-1 (TVA) PWR
900 Aguirre (PRWRA) PWR
660 Bailly Nuclear-1 (North.Ind.Pub.Serv.) BWR
786 Edwin I. Hatch-2 (Ga.Pwr.) BWR
810 William H. Zimmer-1 (CG&E) BWR
875 North Anna-2 (VEPCO) PWR
1156 Salem-2 (Pub.Ser. E&G) PWR
1100 Limerick-1 (Phil.Elect.) BWR
1156 Diablo Canyon-2 (PG&E) PWR
907 Three Mile Island-2 (Metro Ed.) PWR
1096 Don C. Cook-2 (Ind.-Mich. Elect.) PWR
1150 William B. McGuire-1 (Duke Pwr.) PWR
1171 Enrico-Fermi-2 (Detroit Ed.) BWR
855 Brunswick-1 (Car. P&L) BWR
970 Ark. Nuc. One-2 (Ark. P&L) PWR
866 Joseph M. Farley-1 (Ala. Pwr.) PWR
875 North Anna-1 (VEPCO) PWR
906 Davis-Besse (Toledo Ed./Cleve.El.) PWR
1177 Sequoyah-2 (TVA) PWR
1177 Sequoyah-1 (TVA) PWR
1117 Browns Ferry-3 (TVA) BWR
1131 Salem-1 (Pub.Gen.Elect.) PWR
1130 Trojan (Port.Gen.Elect.) PWR
1065 Peach Bottom-3 (Phil. Elect.) BWR
1131 Diablo Canyon-1 (PG&E) PWR
555 Prairie Island-2 (North. States Pwr) PWR
828 Millstone-2 (Millstone Pt.) PWR
845 Hutchinson Island-1 (Fla. P&L) PWR
965 Indian Point-3 (Con.Ed.) PWR
855 Brunswick-2 (Car. P&L) BWR
875 Calvert Cliffs-2 (Balt. G&E) PWR
570 Kewaunee (Wis.Pub.Ser.) PWR
1117 Browns Ferry-2 (TVA) BWR
913 Rancho Seco-1 (SMUD) PWR
853 James A. Fitzpatrick (PASNY) BWR
1065 Peach Bottom-2 (Phil. Elect.) BWR
821 Fort Calhoun-1 (Omaha Pub.Pwr.) PWR
550 Prairie Island-1 (North.States Pwr.) PWR
778 Cooper (Neb. Pub. Pwr.)
Three Mile Island-1
569 Duane Arnold-1 (Iowa Elect. L&P) BWR
1093 Don C. Cook-1 (Ind.-Mich.Elect.) PWR
786 Edwin I. Hatch-1 (Ga. Pwr.) BWR
825 Crystal River-3 (Fla. Pwr.) PWR
882 Beaver Valley-1 (Duquesne) PWR
886 Oconee-3 (Duke Pwr.) PWR
886 Oconee-2 (Duke Pwr.) PWR
1080 Zion-2 (Com.Ed.) PWR
875 Calvert Cliffs-1 (Balt. G&E) PWR
850 Ark. Nuc. One-1 (Ark. P&L) PWR
538 Vermont Yankee (Ver. Yankee Nuc.Pwr.) BWR
Maine Yankee At. Pwr.
497 Point Beach-2 (Wis. Elect.Pwr.) PWR
819 Surry-2 (VEPCO) PWR
819 Surry-1 (VEPCO) PWR
1117 Browns Ferry-1 (TVA) BWR
330 Fort St. Vrain (Pub.Serv.Colo.) HTGR
725 Turkey Point-4 (Fla. P&L) PWR
725 Turkey Point-3 (Fla. P&L) PWR
886 Oconee-1 (Duke Pwr.) PWR
821 Palisades (Consumers Pwr.) PWR
873 Indian Point-2 (Con.Ed.) PWR
1080 Zion-1 (Com.Ed.) PWR
809 Quad Cities-2 (Com.Ed./IIG&E) BWR
809 Quad Cities-1 (Com.Ed./IIG&E) BWR
655 Pilgrim (Boston Ed.) BWR

REACTORS IN OPERATION
PRIOR TO 1972

200 Dresden-1 BWR
809 Dresden-2 BWR
175 Yankee Nuc. PWR
265 Indian Pt.-1 PWR
575 Conn. Yankee PWR
430 San Onofre-1 PWR
650 Oyster Crk-1 BWR
625 Nine Mile Pt BWR
470 R.E.Ginna-1 PWR
652 Millstone-1 BWR
497 Point Beach-1 PWR
730 Robinson-2 PWR
809 Dresden-3 BWR
545 Monticello BWR
380 Six Small Reactors

Excludes
786 NPR-Hanford

1972 1973 1974 1975 1976 1977 1978 1979 1980 1981

120
110
100
90
80
70
60
50
40
30
20
10

pressurized water reactors (PWRs) the 2,150 pounds per square inch of pressure serves to keep the water from turning to steam at a temperature of 620°F. This high-pressure water is conducted from the reactor core, out from a 6-inch steel-clad pressure chamber, by means of huge pipes. These lead to a heat exchanger in which the pressurized water circulates and transfers part of its heat to a steam line leading to a turbogenerator. Conventional methods then convert the steam into electrical power.

A reactor core contains a great mass of fuel—actually, quite enough to run the plant at full power for a year. In a 1,000-megawatt electric plant of conventional design, an equal output would require burning up to 3 million tons of coal. Nuclear fuel "burns" without oxygen and therefore sends no smoke or sulfurous pollutants up a stack, but its compactness has a basic disadvantage. In the event of a pipe break in the water system, the pressurized water would "blow down," and in a matter of ten seconds or so, depending on the nature of the break, the reactor core might be starved for water. Because of its great mass and residual heat, the core cannot remain uncooled very long; water must be gotten to it promptly, otherwise the zircaloy sheath might start to melt and the core could undergo a "meltdown." Distortion of the rods in their water channels could inhibit the reentry of water, and the core could undergo a thermal catastrophe.

Bear in mind, this is not a nuclear runaway, or anything akin to an atomic explosion; reactors are designed to prevent such disasters. Reactor engineers have designed a number of safeguards called ECCS (emergency core-cooling systems), whose function is to pump water back into the core. In 1971 the adequacy of these emergency or standby devices was called into question, and the AEC issued new regulations for ECCS. Should even these fail, engineers have attempted to mitigate the consequences by containment systems. In the United States, all power reactors are enclosed in a thick structure of iron or reinforced concrete. This containment is designed to prevent the escape of radioactive material from a ruptured core or pressure vessel and thus confine contamination to the local site.

Assuming that a nuclear reactor functions routinely in generating electric power, it is necessary to replace part of the fuel every year or so. The plant is shut down, the pressure vessel is opened by removing its upper dome and remote handling equipment is used to extract the central fuel assemblies. New fuel is added, and the spent fuel rods are stored in a deep water vat for several months. After this cooling-off period, the highly radioactive rods are transferred to a heavy shield or cask and transported to one of the five commercial fuel-processing centers. Chemical processing dissolves the solid fuel and removes unburned U-235 and plutonium; the latter is then reprocessed and fabricated as new fuel.

The chemical wastes at reprocessing centers contain huge quantities of radioactive elements that must be disposed of safely. Held in storage for up to ten years, many of the short-lived radioactive species decay to harmless levels; but longer-lived atoms like strontium 90 and cesium 137 lose only a small fraction of their radioactive content in a decade. The AEC studied the waste-disposal problem for almost a quarter-century before it decided to use abandoned salt mines as federal repositories for solidified nuclear waste products. The first repository to be selected was a salt mine, some 1,000 feet below the ground, in central Kansas. This site was abandoned in 1972, and the AEC is holding in abeyance its plans for ultimate disposal of its high-level rad-wastes.

Although the present water reactors do produce some plutonium, part of which is burned in the original fuel rod and part of which is recovered from the spent rod, only 1 percent, or at most 2 percent, of the uranium is utilized as fuel. We have seen that fissioning of all the atoms in a pound of uranium would produce the heat equivalent of burning 2.5 million pounds of coal; but if 1 percent utilization is all we can get, the figure shrinks to 25,000 pounds, or 12.5 tons, of coal. Our projected role of nuclear power for the next three decades requires that it substitute for the burnup of perhaps 25 billion tons of coal. This would mean, figured on a pure statistical basis of one pound of uranium equaling 12.5 tons of coal, that U.S. nuclear burning would consume a million tons of uranium. This understates the uranium requirement because in practice the U_3O_8 feed material for a 1,000-megawatt nuclear plant is about 150 tons per year. Nonetheless, going on the basis of a million tons, does the United States have such uranium reserves in sight?

The 1971 data on uranium reserves show that domestic-proved reserves total 246,000 tons of uranium oxide (U_3O_8) available at $8 per pound, about 200,000 tons of which is found in New Mexico and Wyoming in ores averaging roughly 0.2 percent of uranium oxide. The potential reserves available at $8 per pound run to 490,000 tons, and this number grows to 680,000 tons if the price is boosted to $10. If higher prices are allowed, then lower-grade ores can be worked and correspondingly larger reserves become available. For example, in central Tennessee and extending over some 40,000 square miles of adjoining states, the Chattanooga shale deposits are known to contain about 0.007 percent U_3O_8. They also contain about 8 gallons of oil per ton. A Bureau of Mines study released in 1971 estimated that 71 billion tons of shale might be processed to recover 2.5 million tons of U_3O_8 at a price of about $70 per pound. This high-priced uranium could not compete with coal as fuel for water reactors, and one is led to the dismal conclusion that U.S. domestic resources seem inadequate to support a full-blown nuclear-power industry later in this century. In effect, our natural resources would be incapable of sustaining the spectacular growth predicted for nuclear power.

Scientists have understood this limitation on nuclear-power development from the outset, and as early as 1945 Enrico Fermi, who spearheaded the development of wartime reactors, observed, "The country which first develops a breeder reactor will have a great competitive advantage in atomic energy." By that he meant that if a reactor could be developed to breed more nuclear fuel than it burns, it would remove price limits from uranium fuel and make almost unlimited reserves of it available. Such a reactor is known today, as it was then, as a power-breeder.

The power-breeder, a more difficult technical development than the water reactor, is still not a reality. However, in 1971 President Nixon assigned the highest priority to the development of a demonstration power-breeder, and it is expected that one or two prototype plants, to be completed in the late seventies, will pave the way for construction of commercial power-breeders beginning after 1984.

The great virtue of the power-breeder is that it raises the utilization of uranium from 1 percent to about 70 percent. In effect, this makes available seventy times as much nuclear fuel from the same amount of U_3O_8 because in each fuel cycle more plutonium is produced than is consumed in the power plant. The doubling time for a reactor will depend on the breeder design and on its power rating, but it is expected to be twelve years or less. With such a doubling time, there is no long-term difficulty in fueling power-breeders in the year 2000 or at any time in the next century.

Only a microscopic bit of plutonium existed in the fall of 1942—about one ten-millionth of an ounce, or just barely enough to weigh on a special microbalance devised at the code-named "Metallurgical Laboratory," the A-bomb project's research facility on the University of Chicago campus. Dr. Glenn T. Seaborg headed up a team of chemists who studied the new element and devised procedures to scale up test-tube experiments aimed at separating many pounds of plutonium from highly radioactive solutions.

The codiscoverer of many nuclear species of elements lying beyond uranium in the periodic system, Dr. Seaborg subsequently received the Nobel Prize and in 1961 was appointed chairman of the AEC, a position he filled until 1971. As AEC chief, Seaborg championed development of the power-breeder, the technological marvel that promises an abundant supply of cheap power in the future. The same scientist who in 1942 strained to measure an incredibly small amount of plutonium was to say in 1970: "The material value of all the plutonium fuel in existence in 2000 will approximate $18 billion."

What kind of machine is it that will simultaneously burn and breed so much nuclear fuel? It goes by the acronym LMFBR, standing for Liquid Metal Fast Breeder Reactor. The liquid metal in this case is sodium, the element of choice to replace water as a coolant. Sodium is a light metal that burns spontaneously if exposed to air and causes fireworks if tossed into water—properties that force reactor designers to be extremely cautious in making plans for LMFBRs. Sodium can carry away much more heat from a reactor core than water can, and it is also infinitely better than water in another respect. Water serves two purposes in reactors: It cools and at the same time it slows down or moderates the high-speed (fast) neutrons given off in nuclear fission. In a breeder reactor, designers want to avoid slowing down the neutrons. Sodium cools without slowing down. Although a power-breeder design is possible with slowed-down neutrons, the fast design has been selected by AEC experts, and by scientists in other countries, as the preferred approach to breeding.

The LMFBR consists of a core that is physically smaller than the core of a water reactor, even though it will match its power. Other than being smaller and using a different coolant, the LMFBR is not much different from a water reactor. Liquid sodium emerges from the pressure vessel, then passes to a heat exchanger in which it gives up its heat to another sodium loop, which then goes to a sodium-water heat exchanger. But it is still heat that is being parlayed into electricity through the intermediary of a steam boiler and a turbogenerator. There is less nuclear fuel in the core in the LMFBR, about a ton or so of plutonium in a 15 percent pure form, the rest being uranium. Because the fast chain reaction is used, about 20 percent of the energy released comes from fast fission of uranium-238, the rest from plutonium.

The AEC's plutonium strategy is to bring the power-breeder into commercial use in the mid-1980s, when it will be fueled with plutonium accumulating from water-reactor production. Water reactors will continue to be constructed for utilities, but at a declining rate after 1990. One AEC projection for the future shows about 150 water reactors being built in the 1980–90 decade against a total of about 100 power-breeders. All these reactors are assumed to be of the 1,000-megawatt electric-power capacity. For the 1990–2000 decade, this AEC estimate projects about 60 water re-actors and 275 LMFBRs. After the year 2000, the power-breeder is assumed to be the utility choice when the plu-tonium economy comes into full flower. These estimates must be considered highly optimistic since it will be 1984 before utilities can sense the economic worth of the breeder, and not until the 1990s that engineered plants can come into oper-ation on a significant scale.

There is little doubt that the United States, and other na-tions as well, banks heavily on the power-breeder as a prime source of energy to sustain the nation's economy in the last decades of this century and as the bulwark of its BTUs in the next century. I think there is good reason to believe that the Atomic Energy Commission and the nuclear industry will conquer the technology of the power-breeder, but it remains to be seen whether the new development will reach such a state of perfection that it will be economically attractive to utilities.

This unprecedented rise in the use of a new fuel—one undreamed of before 1940—is such a dramatic innovation in energy release that laymen may be justified in believing that scientists will come up with solutions to all our energy problems. I was reminded of this when I was shopping for a new car in 1972 and the salesman talked about the pollu-tion propensities of the gasoline engine. When I asked him what he thought automobiles would use for fuel in the future, he replied, "Oh, they'll develop an atomic engine small enough to fit under the hood." Nothing I could say would shake his faith in that possibility. Admiral Rickover's dream of nuclear propulsion came true, but only because the energy requirements for running a submarine were modest and its hull was large enough to accommodate the bulk and weight of a nuclear engine. Besides, the U.S. Navy did not have to worry about the economics involved. Utilities have to worry about costs, and in the case of nuclear-power plants, they also have to be concerned with unwanted by-products of reactors, namely, the radioactive substances generated inside the reactor core.

Nuclear power has an enduring disadvantage—radioactivity must be guarded against at every step in the fuel cycle, from the moment ore is taken from the earth to the time when solidified wastes are interred. Scientists have been pursuing a protracted research program to tap a new nuclear-energy source that promises unlimited energy with reduced radioactive hazards. This source is fusion power, or light-element energy, released when atoms (such as hydrogen) combine to form helium. Because the atoms must be speeded up or heated to high energy in order to produce this synthesis, we speak of the process as a *thermo*nuclear reaction.

The universe runs on thermonuclear energy. The stars, among which our sun is a modest example, derive their heat from the thermonuclear burning of elements. Our sun burns ordinary hydrogen in its core to produce helium. This is an extremely slow-paced thermonuclear reaction, so our sun is a well-behaved heat source, with plenty of hydrogen fuel to keep its whole system warm for billions of years. To make thermonuclear power a reality on earth, man must outdo the sun, forcing fusion to speed up its time cycle. That would be utterly impossible using ordinary hydrogen, but, fortunately, there are two other forms of hydrogen that combine more speedily to form helium. One is heavy hydrogen (technically deuterium), and the other is extraheavy hydrogen, or tritium.

Heavy hydrogen occurs in nature to the extent of 1 part to every 6,500 atoms of ordinary hydrogen. Water consists of H_2O, that is, two atoms of hydrogen to one of oxygen, but the form of water incorporating deuterium (D) is a special kind called heavy water. It may be separated from ordinary water by a distillation technique, and it can be mass-produced in rather pure form at modest cost. Decomposition of the heavy water then provides a ready source of heavy hydrogen.

Tritium is both more difficult and more costly to produce; it involves a nuclear process in which atoms of lithium are bombarded with neutrons. A nuclear reaction produces tritium, and since neutrons are most easily produced in a reactor, tritium usually originates at reactor sites. A radioactive atom, tritium has a half-life of twelve years—a given 100 units of tritium in 1972 will have decreased to 50 by 1984 and to 25 by 1996.

In principle, the fusion of deuterium and tritium to produce helium is very simple; it yields an atom of helium and a spare neutron. The energy of the reaction is largely carried off by the neutron, which is called a "very fast" neutron, since it runs away with 14 million electron-volts of fusion energy. The atoms of deuterium have to be heated to very high temperatures—more than 100 million degrees Centigrade—to make them stick together. That is far higher than the temperature of the innermost part of our sun, and its attainment in the laboratory is a major challenge to fusion physicists.

U.S. research on fusion has been going on for over two decades and has not yet proved the scientific feasibility of a fusion reactor, despite the almost $0.5 billion that the AEC has committed to it. One of the difficulties is that the physicists have had to deal with a plasma that they have had little experience with. (A plasma is a gas stripped of atomic electrons, i.e., ionized, so that it forms the fourth state of matter.) A fusion reaction can be achieved only from a dilute plasma of deuterium and tritium, which is so tenuous as to approach a vacuum. The electrically charged atoms (ions) of hydrogen must then be manipulated by means of electric and magnetic fields, so that they are heated to high temperature and confined to a small space within the fusion reactor long enough for significant amounts of fusion energy to be released.

A number of different fusion machines have been investigated, but none has yet attained the goal of fusion. Nonetheless, it appears that a fusion machine would look like a enormous doughnut, some yards in radius, within which the gaseous fuel mixture would circulate under the influence of powerful electromagnetic fields. Huge electromagnets would be required to impose the magnetic field on the plasma. The fuel mixture in ionized form would be injected into the toroidal vacuum chamber, driblets at a time, corresponding to the input of fossil fuel to a steam boiler's firebox, so that in the event of an accident there would be no danger from a large mass of nuclear fuel. From a safety standpoint, a fusion reactor resembles a light bulb—the flick of a switch turns it off. Thus it would be safe to site fusion plants in metropolitan areas.

Trapping the energy of a fusion reaction may eventually involve its direct conversion to electric energy, but the designers are more likely to follow the well-worn rut of all electric plants. That is, they will have to use the energy as a heat source. In a fusion reaction, where the fast neutron runs away with the lion's share of the energy, provision must be made to catch the neutron energy. Evidently the best way to do this is to surround the thin-walled vacuum doughnut with a jacket in which molten lithium is circulated. Neutrons striking the liquid give up their energy in a nuclear reaction that serves to heat the lithium and, at the same time, spawn tritium. The heat is carried outside the reactor by pumping the lithium to a heat exchanger, whence it goes the thermal route to the production of power. The tritium is born as a gas which is piped out of the device to be processed as fuel for the fusion reactor. Thus the fusion reactor is also a breeder; it will produce more tritium than it burns.

Physicists who have studied the fusion-reactor design for many years acknowledge that the device will have to be very large in order to produce power economically. Present estimates put its power rating at a value above 3,000 thermal megawatts. Fusion plants will undoubtedly exacerbate the current trend toward very large central-station power concentrations. It also seems that a concomitant of all central power stations will be the generation of large amounts of heat that must be "dumped" into the local environment.

From a resource standpoint, the fusion machine is an unadulterated dream. The basic fuel is heavy hydrogen, which may be taken from any body of water—a river, a lake, or even an ocean. Extracting the heavy hydrogen simply robs the water of a trace element, leaving the processed water potable. The heavy hydrogen from 2 million gallons of water could fuel a 1,000-megawatt electric-capacity plant for one year. The actual consumption of heavy hydrogen in such a plant would be little more than one ounce per hour. In a coal-fired plant, this same electric capacity would entail the burning of 300 tons of coal in an hour. The United States could be supplied with electricity for the entire twenty-first century by tapping the heavy-hydrogen power of a week's flow of water over Niagara Falls. Fusion power thus has the potential of providing mankind with a virtually inexhaustible supply of energy.

The potential and the reality of fusion power are separated by a research-and-development gap of at least several decades. Once the scientific feasibility of a fusion reactor is established, there will remain the arduous task of engineering a fusion plant to produce a reliable source of power economically. The scientific feasibility of fission power was established a quarter-century before utilities put their faith in nuclear reactors, and the technology of fission machines was firmly laid out in the early postwar period, whereas much of the basic technology of fusion devices is still below the horizon.

Although fusion will be a much cleaner source of power than fission, the core of a heavy-hydrogen burner will become intensely radioactive, and the large amount of tritium generated daily will pose a radioactive hazard of considerable magnitude. But from both a resource and a safety standpoint, fusion power, if it can be realized, stands out as man's best source of electric energy for the future.

CHAPTER

5

THE CONSUMER AVALANCHE

The affluence of the U.S. society is reflected in Figure 5-1, which shows the percentage of homes possessing a variety of consumer products. Apart from a natural desire most people have for acquiring creature comforts, the United States has accentuated this desire through a barrage of advertising promotions which use every available medium to persuade the consumer that gadget X or product Y must be purchased. Americans have become conditioned to buy novelty, and a huge advertising business, symbolized by the two words *Madison Avenue,* has grown up to promote sales. Furthermore, the most potent of these advertising displays, the television screen, is a self-inflicted medium. When a new gadget first hits the market, its sales curve is dizzyingly steep (Figs. 5-2 and 5-3), but after five to ten years, the curve begins to bend over. The market has reached the saturation point; sales are made mainly to those setting up housekeeping for the first time and those who want replacements.

Mechanical refrigerators remain the most popular of twentieth-century innovations. Almost every American home now has one. Yet many a man alive still remembers the daily ritual of sticking the ice company's square card in the living-room window, with the appropriate number of pounds at

107

the top, as a signal to the driver on the route. In fact, the iceman—armed with his pick and his tongs—survived even the horse as an urban institution. The ice companies had converted to trucks before Frigidaires swamped them. After a precipitous ten-year growth, sales of electric refrigerators bent over in the thirties to about 5 million a year—and remain there.

There are even more of us who watched, with the heedless indifference of youth, as the first of the electronic media

FIGURE 5-1

THE ELECTRIFIED U.S. HOME

The bars representing refrigerators and radios are both nudging the 100 percent barrier. Sales of these from now on will be—as they have been for some time—to homes that are newly established, to homes that need replacements, or to homes that want two or more of the items. The inevitable increase in electricity consumption will come from the lengthening of the short bars at the bottom of the graph.

FIGURE 5-1

THE ELECTRIFIED U.S. HOME

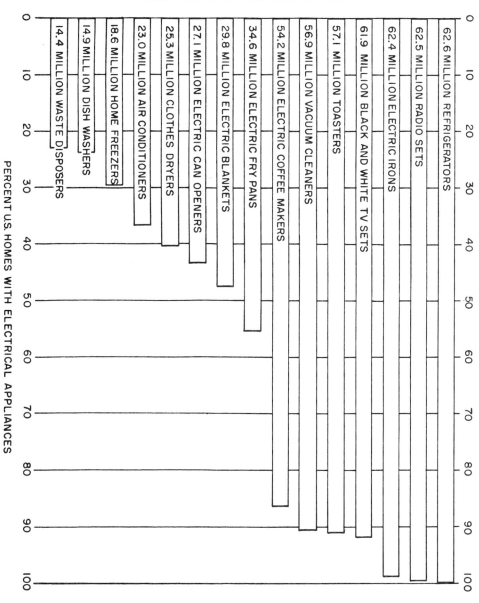

began its transformation of the American style of living. In 1922 my mechanical-minded father installed a radio set in our house—the first one on our block. It was a large box featuring a bewildering array of calibrated dials and a huge horn that sprouted above the set. It was powered by a set of wet storage batteries that my father ministered to in the basement. For a while, our family attained a new popularity in the neighborhood, but we lost the advantage in a couple of years as less-challenging versions of our electronic wonder became available.

FIGURE 5-2

U.S. PRODUCTION OF REFRIGERATORS, FREEZERS, AND FROZEN FOOD

The curve for electric-refrigerator production started bending over after a ten-year boom. The home-freezer market was saturated in about five years. Freezer sales are consistently lower because of the limited appeal to small families and to apartment dwellers and because of the initial cost—to the poor. Frozen-food sales follow the population curve.

FIGURE 5-2

U.S. PRODUCTION OF REFRIGERATORS, FREEZERS, AND FROZEN FOOD

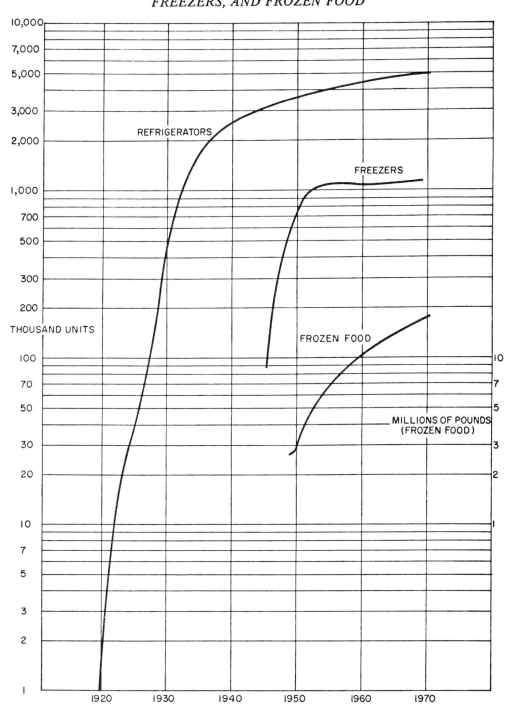

Television made its commercial debut in the late forties, and by 1949 a million U.S. homes had TV sets. Now nearly every home has at least one. Color TV came along fifteen years later and is undergoing the same heady growth. U.S. production of color-TV sets exceeded a million in 1964 and reached 6 million four years later (Fig. 5-3). Once color TV invaded the U.S. household, Madison Avenue was firmly implanted and was in a strategic location not only to influence consumer habits but on a far greater scale to subject tens of

FIGURE 5-3

U.S. HOMES WITH RADIO AND TELEVISION

The radio sales curve began to wilt slightly during the Depression, but it continued to ascend. One million U.S. homes had TV sets by 1949; there were 10 million in 1951; and 64 million black-and-white units were produced in the United States in the decade ending in 1970. In 1965 black-and-white sales reached their peak—8.4 million sets. Since then color TV has led in sales.

FIGURE 5-3

U.S. HOMES WITH RADIO AND TELEVISION

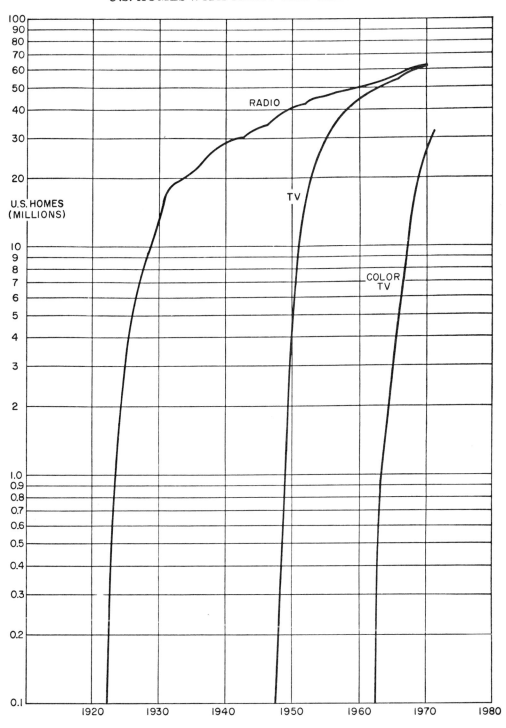

millions of people to intimate manipulation of their way of life. The combination of ear-eye appeal and the dynamics of colored display was to have a momentous impact on the lives of almost all Americans.

An increase in the number of electric items in the American household is ineluctably accompanied by a dual increase in the demand for electricity—first for their manufacture, then for their operation. Additional increments of energy are obviously required for input materials, transportation, and merchandising the products. These all add to the capital BTU costs of the items. Spectacular growth in sales of any one item is always matched by an equally spectacular jump in electric-power consumption. To suppose that Americans can make any real dent in the energy-consumption curve by using restraint in operating the equipment they own is to fail to understand the percentages in Figure 5-1. Turning your air conditioner off at night is commendable, but it will not offset the load added by one of your neighbors who may be installing air conditioning this summer for the first time. It is the previously underelectrified homes that will keep the energy-consumption curve soaring.

Following the route of some of our natural resources from their raw state to the junk heap is instructive as to how consumer demands affect the resource reserves and the state of the biosphere.

Aluminum production, for example, is called an energy-intensive industry—one that consumes large amounts of electric energy. Aluminum production in the United States is illustrated in Figure 5-4. Aluminum is obtained from bauxite, an ore running 50 to 60 percent aluminum oxide (Al_2O_3) which has to be reduced electrolytically, that is, by passing large amounts of electric current through a "pot" in which molten metal evolves at a temperature of 1,800°F. It takes somewhat less than 10 kilowatt-hours of electricity to produce 1 pound of aluminum metal, and it is expected that this will drop below an 8:1 ratio by the year 2000. Even so, the production of 60 million tons of aluminum in the year

2000 would mean the consumption of almost 1 trillion kilo-watt-hours of electric energy, or as much as the United States used for all purposes in 1964, and a tenth of that projected for the year 2000. The U.S. Bureau of Mines esti-mate, made in 1970, projects a low of 18.5 million and a high of 37 million tons of primary aluminum for the year 2000. Although significantly less than our "straight-line" extrapolation, the official estimate predicts that society's continued preference for the versatile metal will consume 5 percent of the U.S. total energy in the year 2000.

Does the United States have enough bauxite to keep its pot lines turning out the required flow of aluminum? Domestic supply of bauxite concentrates in Arkansas where there are 45 million tons of known reserves, with a potential total of 300 million tons for the entire United States. However, it will be necessary to devise new processes to tap the potential of lower-grade ores, that is, those running less than 50 percent alumina content. These cannot now compete with imported bauxite, which accounts for 85 percent of the U.S. supply. The United States which uses about half the world's bauxite, imports principally from the Caribbean countries—Jamaica, Haiti, and the Dominican Republic—and from northeastern South America. The combination of a low-cost supply line and cheap electric power contributes to the dominance of the United States in aluminum production.

U.S. reserves of high-grade aluminum-containing ore are not adequate for its near-term demands, and even the 215-million-ton aluminum content of Caribbean and South American reserves falls far short of the nearly half-billion-ton consumption that is probable for the next three decades. This means that unless new resources are found, new technologies will have to be exploited to utilize lower-grade ores.

Much more essential to the continued flow of consumer products is the base metal iron, whose early history in the United States was keyed to the great deposits of high-grade ore in the Minnesota Mesabi range. These seemingly inexhaustible ore beds funneled their surface-mined high-grade ore to Lake Superior, whence it was shipped to Gary, Indiana, and other great American steel centers. This single ore source made the United States the leading iron producer of the world and continued to supply over 80 percent of the national requirement until the mid-century. I remember driving through the Mesabi region and being awed by the manmade mountains created by the uniform, parallel piles of ore spoils stretching to the horizon. But so great was the U.S. need for the primary structural material that even the Mesabi

FIGURE 5-4

U.S. ALUMINUM PRODUCTION (1900–1970)

A straight edge joining the data points of primary aluminum production from 1910 to 1970 shows that the rate of growth for the sixty-year period is about 9 percent, for an eight-year doubling time, or a 220-fold increase. If that growth rate extends to the year 2000, the U.S. will be producing 60 million tons of aluminum that year.

FIGURE 5-4

U.S. ALUMINUM PRODUCTION (1900–1970)

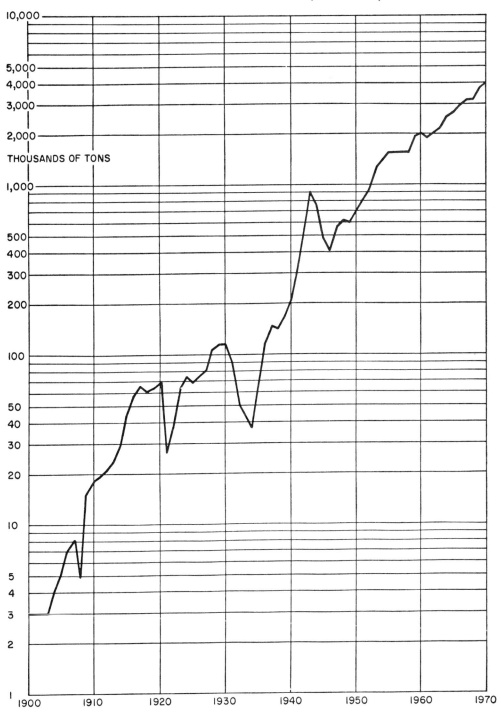

deposits were worked out, and shortly after World War II the country was no longer self-sufficient in its iron-ore supply. Nothing so clearly marks the gyrations of the business cycle as the periodic dips in iron-ore production, as shown in Figure 5-5. The future growth rate for iron production will probably run about 2 percent per year: There is no drastic demand on ore supplies in sight. Although the high-grade Minnesota ores have been depleted, lower-grade taconite ores are being exploited in competition with foreign ore. There is a sufficient world reserve of iron ore to provide for at least a full century's consumption.

FIGURE 5-5

U.S. IRON-ORE PRODUCTION (1900–1970)
(Plus Net Imports)

The checkered history of iron-ore production yields an erratic growth curve. During the first two decades of this century, production rose at a rate of less than 3 percent. It slumped in the early 1920s and then struggled upward, but it did not regain its World War I peak before skidding to less than 10 million tons in 1932. The Mesabi deposits were worked out by the end of World War II, and the country began to rely more heavily on imports. Import tonnage after the mid-century is represented on the graph.

FIGURE 5-5

U.S. IRON-ORE PRODUCTION (1900–1970)
(Plus Net Imports)

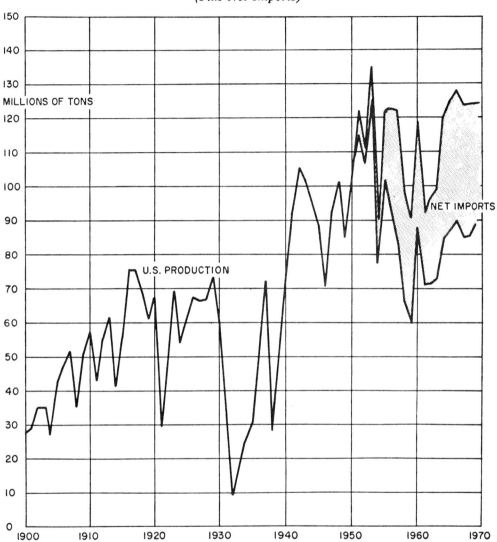

Metal-processing plants pose worrisome environmental threats, specifically to air and water. Air pollution from iron and steel plants is coming under tight control, and it is expected that the hazard will be abated in the future. Their water-pollution threat is two-pronged: first, thermal—from the heat of coolant water; and second, chemical—from the pickup of contaminants in processing. A steel mill may require between 10,000 and 50,000 gallons of water for each ton of metal processed. Steel mills, like power plants, should operate at closed cycles, using cooling towers, or other cooling techniques to insure that iron processing does not involve thermal pollution. This is important because U.S. iron production in 1970 accounted for 6 percent of U.S. energy consumption.

The use of water in the United States is illustrated in Figure 5-6, where there is plotted a record of use for irrigation.

FIGURE 5-6

U.S. WATER USE (1900–2000)

Three of the four categories of water use (as these categories are defined by the U.S. government) follow roughly general patterns, and they will probably do so for the rest of the century. The use of water in steam-electric utilities, however (second line from bottom at left in graph), has increased at a rate of about 5 percent per year. It surpassed all other "industrial-commercial" uses combined in 1950 and amounted to 48 trillion gallons in 1970. The bend-over thereafter is due to an increased use of cooling towers and the siting of plants near coasts, where sea water can be used as a coolant.

FIGURE 5-6

U.S. WATER USE (1900–2000)

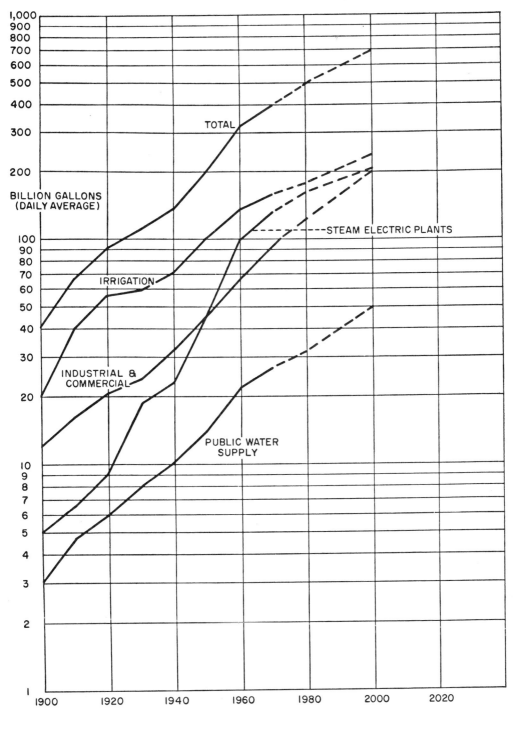

industry and commerce including a separate curve for utility operations and for public water supply. Water has been used for steam-electric plants at an increasing rate of about 5 percent per year, roughly paralleling the rapid growth of power plants. For the most part, utilities have chosen to use "once-through" cooling for their steam plants, a practice that requires the intake of large quantities of water, especially where the water temperature rise is modest. If the use of water for steam plants had continued at the rate of the 1940–60 period, the nation's electric plants would today be using more water than is diverted to irrigation.

The bend-over of the curve representing steam-plant water use and its lower growth rate in the future is due to the increasing use of cooling towers and to the siting of new plants in coastal locations where seawater is utilized as a coolant. Many steam-electric plants are now located on major rivers, where the heat discharged dissipates itself as the water moves downstream, and a stream's water may be used more than once for cooling purposes. Even so, the total complex of U.S. electric plants will use a sixth of the total fresh water runoff of the nation by the end of the century.

Figure 5-6 is quite different from others we have presented in that it represents the use of a renewable resource. This might be a cheering thought if the amount of rain falling on the nation were not fixed as a statistical average; man still must learn to maintain a strict set of books on water withdrawals from the fresh water runoff. The passage of water-control and water-quality improvement acts by Congress has provided the legislative means for federal agencies to curb excess pollution of the nation's water and to prevent overheating of streams, rivers, lakes, and estuaries.

U.S. industry routinely uses many metals in relatively small amounts (compared with iron and aluminum, or even copper and lead), which have recently come under scrutiny because of their suspected toxicity in the biosphere. Mercury, for example, is used industrially to the extent of about

3,000 tons per year. It is the silvery metal liquid used in thermometers and, in much larger quantities, in batteries and lamps and especially in the production of chlorine. Ultimately, mercury finds its way to rivers, lakes, and seas and is taken up by microorganisms whose growth is accelerated by the assimilation of industrial, metropolitan, and agricultural wastes. Fish feeding on these mercury-tainted organisms accumulate mercury, and sometimes, notably in Japan, people who eat fish and shellfish suffer acute mercury poisoning and death. Even low levels of mercury concentration can have damaging effects on human beings. The World Health Organization has set a level of 0.5 parts per million (ppm) as the safe maximum concentration of mercury in human food. U.S. authorities banned the sale of swordfish in 1971 when it was found that these predators had accumulated mercury in concentrations exceeding that maximum. The Environmental Protection Agency has extended its surveillance of potentially harmful heavy metals to include vanadium (used in steel), cadmium (needed for batteries and electroplating), lead, and arsenic.

Paradoxically, a few very hazardous materials have been deliberately introduced into the environment (Fig. 5-7). They are the chemical compounds, products of World War II research, used to control agricultural pests. Previously, simple compounds like copper sulfate were the insecticides of choice; 134 million pounds of copper sulfate were produced in 1939. Pyrethrum, a louse-control agent, was imported from Japan and Yugoslavia, where the perennial herb *Chrysanthemum cinerariaefolium* is indigenous. Red squill, a small plant found in Mediterranean countries, has a bulb whose powdered form is useful in rodent control. War requirements forced scientists to look for substitute products and to mass-produce substances like DDT, whose insecticidal properties were recognized in 1939. DDT first achieved fame for its success in stopping a typhus epidemic in Italy in 1943–44.

Our graph of pesticide use clearly documents the agricultural demand for agents to reduce the ravages caused by insects and other plant enemies. The synthesis of organic pesticides was heralded as the means to victory in the war against all major insect pests, and health authorities saw in DDT an instrument for eliminating malaria. More potent than pyrethrum, which had eradicated malaria in some parts of Brazil before the war, DDT appeared to be the hero in the final chapter of the story of man's constant combat with nature. Moreover, the DDT adventure was merely the beginning of the chapter; research soon expanded the number of

FIGURE 5-7

U.S. USE OF PESTICIDES

The top line of this graph, which shows the growth of the use of all pesticides since World War II, includes herbicides and rodenticides. An increased use of these chemicals by farmers accounts for the contrast in the top and middle lines since the early 1960s, when the use of DDT was curtailed. Most of the DDT now produced in this country is exported (bottom line) for use in malaria control.

FIGURE 5-7

U.S. USE OF PESTICIDES

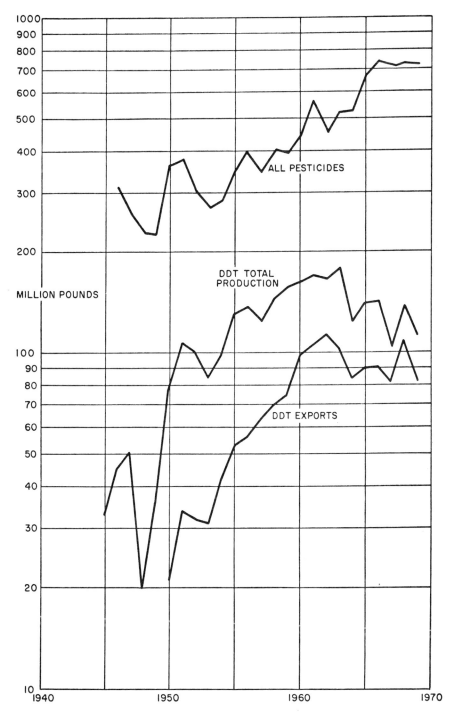

organic insecticidal compounds to nine hundred, formulated in over sixty thousand preparations. The dollar value of U.S.-produced pesticides, $440 million in 1964, topped the $1 billion level in the late sixties and seemed headed for new highs.

Insecticides, in particular, sold briskly, since DDT and such other chlorinated hydrocarbons as aldrin-dieldrin found wide application in controlling the insects afflicting food and fiber crops. Aldrin, whose chemical name is hexachlorohexahydroendoexodimethanonaphthalene, was used as a soil insecticide for over half the U.S. corn crop. Herbicides, such as 2,4-D, a merciful acronym for 2,4-dichlorophenoxyacetic acid, became another powerful weapon of chemical assault on weed pests, along with 2,4,5-T (trichlorophenoxyacetic acid). Indeed, so potent were they that concentrated mixtures of them were used, under the code name Agent Orange, as defoliants in Vietnam. The military demands for certain organic herbicides exceeded U.S. production capacity in 1967 and induced a shortage of 2,4-D and 2,4,5-T for the agricultural market.

Make no mistake about it—the new chemical agents did the job they were meant to do. DDT was widely used in India, Brazil, Nepal, Thailand, and other countries to wipe out the malarial mosquito, a difficult assignment. A malarial victim may infect mosquitoes for many months, and it is therefore essential to interrupt the infective cycle for long periods of time. DDT is ideal for the purpose: It is extremely persistent besides being cheap and easy to use. But it was its very persistence that made it a potential hazard for man and his environment.

DDT is chemically resistant to change, that is, it retains its chemical and toxic identity long after it is released to the environment. It is called a *hard* pesticide because experiments indicate that it remains toxic for at least twenty years after initial use. This lingering toxicity is compounded when the contamination of water, air, and soil results in a concentration of the pesticide through a buildup process that can be extremely subtle and complex. For example, microorganisms in a marine environment may feed on a pesticide level of several parts per billion (ppb) of DDT. However, an oyster pumping in these organisms can concentrate the DDT as much as seventy thousand times. Similarly, small fish may build up levels of hundreds of parts per million (ppm) of DDT in their flesh, and even higher concentrations in their organs and viscera. These, in turn, may be eaten by aquatic birds, such as herons, pelicans, and gulls. Thus DDT builds up in predators from successive concentrations in the links of the food chain.

The detrimental effects of DDT accumulation are, of course, now well-known; wide publicity has attended tragic losses in populations of birds and marine life. Depending on the species, the DDT concentration may kill the bird or fish directly, or it may intercept a critical link in the reproduction cycle: It has produced extensive fish kills in the lower Mississippi River and in marshlands, and it has endangered the reproduction of the brown pelican, common to the southwestern United States, by thinning the eggshells to a point where they are simply membranes, lacking in calcium. In other species, a 20 percent reduction in eggshell thickness has led to shell cracking in incubation and to subsequent interdiction of the reproduction cycle. DDT has been found to be lethal to fish larvae at levels of concentration tolerated by the egg parent without ill effect.

Mackerel harvested off the coast of California had to be taken off the market because DDT concentrations exceeded the 5 ppm guideline laid down as the limit safe for human food. During 1966–68 bald eagles found dead in western states contained high levels of dieldrin and DDT; some actually had lethal concentrations of dieldrin in the brain.

How does all of this affect man? A 1971 report of the U.S. Council on Environmental Quality states: "The average young American child contains about five parts per million

DDT. The content in older persons is slightly higher. DDT and other pesticides have been observed to cause measurable changes in body chemistry. However, there is no conclusive evidence that pesticide dosages found in the environment, or even dosages several times the normal exposure, lead to any increase in disease or illness."

Nonetheless, the situation was serious enough for the secretary of Health, Education, and Welfare to set up a task force on Pesticides and Their Relationship to Environmental Health, which reported in December 1969 and made wide-ranging recommendations. It concluded its study with this paragraph:

> To sum up, the field of pesticide toxicology exemplifies the absurdity of a situation in which 200 million Americans are undergoing lifelong exposure, yet our knowledge of what is happening to them is at best fragmentary and for the most part indirect and inferential. While there is little ground for forebodings of disaster, there is even less for complacency. The proper study of mankind is man. It is to this study that we should address ourselves without delay.

Specifically, the task force indicted a number of pesticides, recommending that "persistent chlorinated hydrocarbons which have a broad spectrum of biological effects, including DDT, DDD, aldrin, chlordane, dieldrin, endrin, heptachlor, and toxaphene, should be progressively removed from general use over the next two years."

The U.S. use of DDT has dropped sharply (Fig. 5-7); most of it produced here goes to exports. The United States has no malarial control problem, but other nations depend on DDT for this purpose. As the World Health Organization has pointed out, "Limitations on the use of DDT would give rise to greater problems in the majority of the developing countries."

The HEW task force's reminder that the proper study of

128

mankind is man had a cruel twist. Man, today, contains from five to eight parts of DDT per million, but this is a low level, not amenable to any direct study on man, and far too low for health surveys to turn up any significant effects; indeed, it is too early to expect any. In this respect, DDT is analogous to radioactive fallout. Small quantities of cesium 137 and strontium 90 are measurable in all human beings. They are, in fact, most readily measured in the Lapps, who subsist on reindeer meat, which is high in the cesium 137 that concentrates in lichen on which the reindeer browse. Yet the levels of radioactivity are so low, compared with radiation dosage received from natural sources, that it is hopeless to try to establish any correlation between the body burden of cesium 137 and strontium 90 and signs of disease.

Lacking any substantive data on the long-term or chronic effects of pesticides, the U.S. government has taken a series of steps to restrict the hazards. These have included banning the use of DDT, aldrin, 2,4,5-T, dieldrin, DDD, mercury compounds, and other pesticides for certain crops. In addition, the Environmental Protection Agency is undertaking the establishment of a nationwide monitoring system to provide effective surveillance of the environment and food supply. One of the great virtues of the EPA organization is that for the first time it provides the nation with a centralized means of systems analysis—for looking at the total environment rather than at bits and pieces of it.

The ultimate aspect of consumption is waste disposal. The average American family is guilty of little direct air pollution and probably thinks little about household effluents in the form of flushed wastes. More visible to the householder is the weekly accumulation of the solid wastes—paper, garbage, cans, bottles, grass clippings, worn-out appliances—that is picked up by the trash collector. In a sense, the American home has become a way station for the flood of consumer products, many of which are engineered to obsolesce rather quickly.

129

One ubiquitous U.S. waste product is too large to cram into a garbage can: Many Americans simply abandon old cars on the city streets. In New York City during 1971, some eighty-two thousand old automobiles were left at curbsides for the city to tow away (Fig. 5-8). Extrapolation of this trend to even 1980 would be dangerous for any chartist, but some authorities are so worried that they have proposed requiring car buyers to make a deposit to cover the expense of final disposal of the vehicle.

FIGURE 5-8

NEW YORK CITY'S ABANDONED CARS

A mess-making combination of affluence and apathy has bequeathed to New York City an immense fleet of rejected automobiles within the last decade. In 1971 alone, the city towed 82,000 abandoned cars off its streets. That was more than an eightfold increase over 1963.

FIGURE 5-8

NEW YORK CITY'S ABANDONED CARS

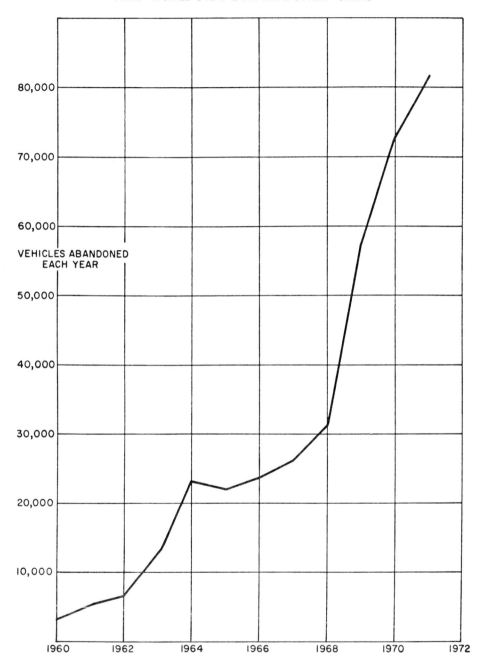

The containers of some home products, like bottled drinks, circulate on a deposit basis to encourage their return to industry. Here New York City's experience with a new 16-ounce Pepsi-Cola bottle is not inspiring. Some 14 million of the bottles required a nickel deposit, but within a short time, a survey showed that most of them ended up in the city dumps. Most Americans prefer to use cans and nonreturnable bottles designed to end up in the family trash can. Refuse accumulation in urban areas amounts to five pounds per person daily, and it is estimated that this will rise to eight pounds by 1980. By 1980, in short, each American family will be adding five tons of solids to the national waste heap in a single year. Today the nation's scrap pile embraces, at any given time, about 100 million rubber tires, 30 billion glass bottles, double that number of cans, and millions of tons of paper and plastic.

The Bureau of Solid Waste Management of the Health, Education, and Welfare Department estimates that 75 percent of all collected solid wastes is disposed of at some fourteen thousand open garbage dumps and only 13 percent goes to sanitary landfills; almost all the rest is burned. Dump burning pollutes the air, and without proper sanitary practice, open dumps serve as breeding grounds for swarms of rodents, flies, and other pests. Quite apart from the aesthetic and sanitary aspects of improper dumping, there is the gross misuse of valuable resources that remain in aluminum cans and other metallic products and the loss of energy in combustion of paper and wood products. Recycling as a means of conserving resources is just beginning in the United States.

In retrospect, surveying the past century's mode of development, it seems that U.S. producers and consumers have followed a "dig-and-dump" philosophy. From mine to junk heap, we have as a society ignored the environmental impact of our industrialization. A private-enterprise system, seeking to maximize profits, could not be expected to cut into profits to protect the environment—or the consumer. It was only after mid-century that flagrant insults to the environment became so eye compelling that the nation as a whole decided to do something about environmental protection. Passage of the National Environmental Policy Act and the creation of the Environmental Protection Agency stand out as symbols of commitment to environmental reform.

CHAPTER

6

THE KNOWLEDGE EXPLOSION

The widespread realization that unchecked, unmonitored industrial growth threatens the survival of life on this planet has engendered a new kind of anti-intellectualism. The modern antiscience movement recruits its adherents not from the uneducated masses, who know from experience that expanding industry means expanding employment, but from the elite. It is those who have never endured privations who want to halt progress, discard rationality, prevent the acquisition of more knowledge. They accurately attribute the exponential growth curves of the twentieth century to the discovery of new knowledge through scientific research. Scientists themselves are sometimes appalled at the results. I once heard J. Robert Oppenheimer say, only half in jest, "We need new knowledge like we need a hole in the head."

Of course Oppenheimer knew that no threat is dire enough to inhibit the quest for knowledge. Galileo pushed ahead at the peril of his own life, and in fear of eternal damnation. Modern scientists will not halt on the brink of discovering knowledge that could blast us all to hell, and their reason is the same as Galileo's—they will at least know why. Doom is to be preferred over ignorance. The more thoughtful of the new wave of antigrowth polemicists see the folly of striking at the true roots of progress. As one of them, Ross Gelbspan, has written of the zooming growth curve, "There is a positive benefit that too few have spoken about: the growth of knowledge. We know more as a people than any people, at any time in history. Let us begin to use the resource of knowledge." And he proposes that inquiring minds similar to those who brought us to our present pass now direct themselves toward getting us out of it.

FIGURE 6-1

U.S. PRODUCTION OF COLLEGE GRADUATES AND DOCTORATES (1900–1970)

Except for dips during the two World Wars, the growth in the number of both bachelor's and doctor's degrees awarded in the United States has progressed at an annual rate of 7 percent since 1900. The impact of the Depression was reduced by the simultaneous scarcity of jobs for both graduates and undergraduates. Overall, the annual growth rate for baccalaureates has been about 4.5 percent and for doctorates 6.5 percent. The recent surge in doctorates has brought their rate up to about 12 percent. America's far-flung complex of about 2,500 institutions of higher learning is expected to turn out about a million bachelor's degrees during 1976.

FIGURE 6-1

U.S. PRODUCTION OF COLLEGE GRADUATES
AND DOCTORATES (1900–1970)

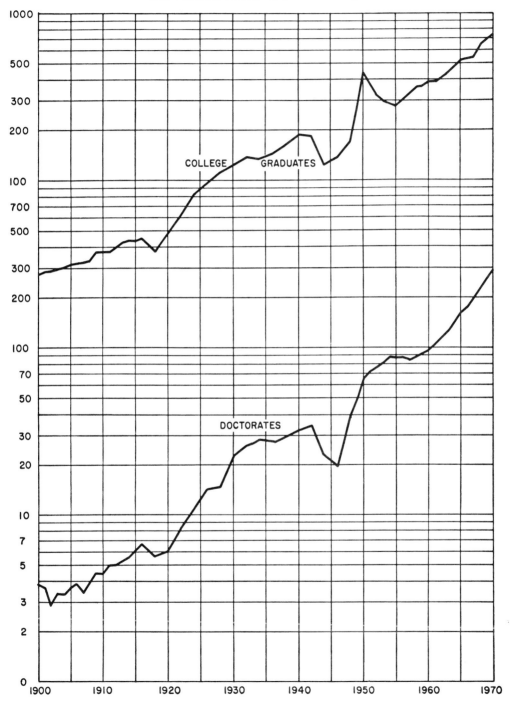

To chart the growth rate of knowledge, I have chosen two of its more tangible manifestations—the number of Ph.D. degrees granted and the number of scientific articles published. Research and development in the United States are directed principally by highly trained individuals, most of whom have doctorates in science and engineering.

Yale University began America's vast production of Ph.D.'s when it awarded its first doctor's degree in 1861. In the next hundred years, U.S. universities awarded 180,000 doctorates, and then almost as many in the next eleven years (Fig. 6-1). The U.S. Office of Education estimates that the next decade will see from 369,000 to 520,000 Ph.D.'s emerging from the campus. However, this assumes that society will find jobs for the new graduates—an assumption not fortified by events in the early seventies when flocks of Ph.D.'s found that their services were not needed.

The buildup of a pool of highly specialized individuals was essential to the massive shift of the U.S. economy from brawn to brain. It was, of course, accelerated by the mechanization of the farm and the movement of people to cities. It would be wrong to correlate the economic growth of the United States with the Ph.D. production curve, especially during the first third of the century when relatively few advanced graduates were engaged in organized research.

In 1900 the U.S. civilian labor force, 26 million strong, was relatively uneducated. Only about a third of the workers were grade school graduates, and only one of every twelve boasted of a high school diploma. The college graduate was in the ratio of 1 to 87, and the Ph.D. in science and engineering was a *rara avis*. Half a century later there was a dramatic change in the educational attainments of the labor force—82 percent had graduated from grade school, 50 percent had a high school education, and 7 percent were college graduates. By 1970 almost all workers had grade school diplomas, 70 percent had four years of high school, and 14 percent had bachelor's degrees.

America's mechanization during the early decades of

this century cannot be attributed to an influx of Ph.D.'s into industry. That was the era of the inventor and entrepreneur —of Thomas A. Edison and Henry Ford—and of skilled engineers, like Charles Kettering. A few giant industrial firms diverted funds to corporate research, but it was primarily product oriented and more of an engineering than a scientific pursuit. As for the U.S. government, it did not sponsor university research, and it provided only token funds to federal scientific activity—mainly in a few research establishments, such as the National Bureau of Standards.

When the United States entered the electronics era in the 1920s, it underwent a quantum jump as a new domain of knowledge needed to be opened up to exploit radio, automatic devices, and control equipment. Gradually the competence of the solitary inventor was challenged, and specialized brainpower was needed for solving technical problems. World War II proved to be the beginning of massive federal funding in support of research and development (Fig. 6-2).

The number of scientists and engineers holding a doctor's degree is now roughly 150,000—over ten times the number in the United States in 1930. The Ph.D.'s represented in Figure 6-1 include all fields, not science alone. But the cutting edge of the U.S. research effort depends on doctorates in chemistry, physics, and mathematics and in the biological sciences. Specialized research in solid-state physics, for example, is limited to highly trained people of Ph.D. caliber. If we include scientists and engineers with master's degrees, or the professional equivalent, then the nation's innovative work force includes a total of about a quarter million individuals. The total work force in science and engineering is about ten times that, but the creativity of the research-and-development community centers largely in its quarter million highly educated members.

A nation that seeks to maintain a competitive position in world trade and that has a highly paid work force must put a premium on technological innovation. Because of the extreme complexity of modern technology, it is essential for many of the best brains to be employed on research that will contribute to the development of new or improved products and techniques useful to the economy. The flattening out of the curve in Figure 6-2 would seem to bode ill for the nation's economic future, but before jumping to this conclusion it is well to consider just how the United States has been spending its research-and-development dollar.

Federal funds for research and development have been directed to the Defense Department, the National Aeronautics

FIGURE 6-2

U.S. GOVERNMENT EXPENDITURES FOR RESEARCH AND DEVELOPMENT (1940–70)

The spectacular growth in government funds spent for research and development in the first half of the 1940s was due to outlays for military projects, including the A-bomb, radar, and proximity fuses. The Korean conflict caused another spurt. The rate of federal R & D spending under Eisenhower and Kennedy approached the phenomenal figure of 18 percent. The boom ended in 1964. From then on the annual federal funding for science and technology rose very slowly to $17 billion, then dipped. Further increases were forestalled by demands from other sectors, notably the military in connection with the Vietnam War.

FIGURE 6-2

U.S. GOVERNMENT EXPENDITURES FOR
RESEARCH AND DEVELOPMENT (1940–70)

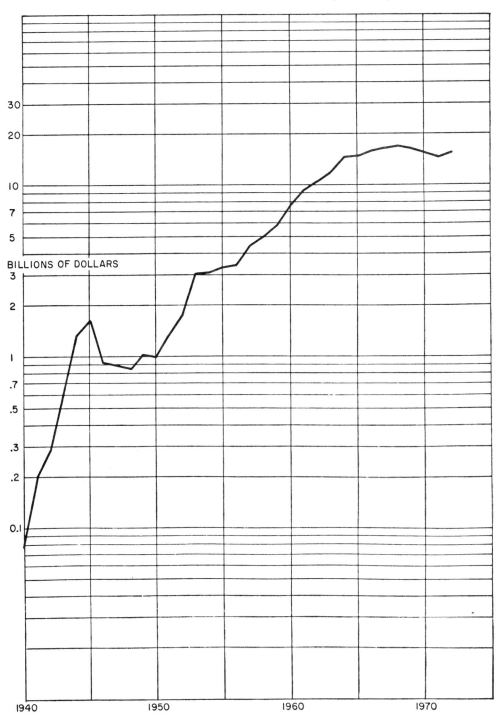

and Space Administration (NASA), and the Atomic Energy Commission (AEC) (Fig. 6-3). There is little doubt that this funding increased the store of technical information in the past dozen years, but the pertinence of the information to the nation's economy is questionable. Military research and development in the past did have a certain payoff for the economy; for example, the development of powerful jet engines for the military served to usher in the commercial jetliner. However, today's military technology bears less and

FIGURE 6-3

FEDERAL RESEARCH AND DEVELOPMENT EXPENDITURES (1958–71)

More than 60 percent of the federal research-and-development funds since 1958 have gone to the Department of Defense (lower portion of chart). The National Aeronautics and Space Administration and the Atomic Energy Commission got most of the rest. Federal spending on all other kinds of scientific research has amounted to 15 percent of the total, on the average.

142

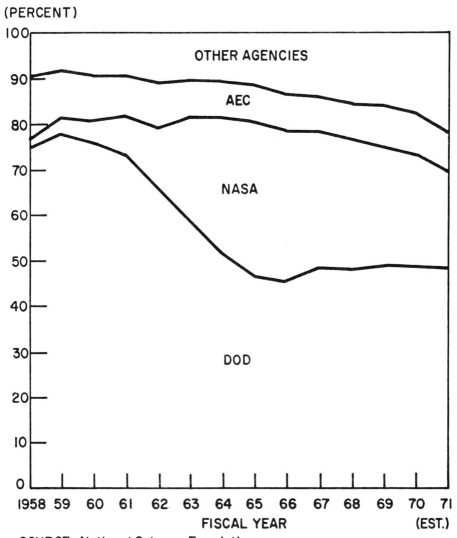

FIGURE 6-3

*FEDERAL RESEARCH AND DEVELOPMENT
EXPENDITURES (1958–71)*

(PERCENT)

OTHER AGENCIES

AEC

NASA

DOD

1958 59 60 61 62 63 64 65 66 67 68 69 70 71

FISCAL YEAR   (EST.)

SOURCE: National Science Foundation

less relation to the marketplace. Intercontinental ballistic missiles, as a case in point, have little relevance for the American consumer. This is not to say that defense R & D produces nothing of value to peacetime pursuits of the nation but that the payoff is very small.

The U.S. space effort has been highly publicized, and NASA has worked hard to convince the public that space funds are a good national investment. Certainly the United States has gained great prestige in being the first to land men on the moon and return them safely to earth, but the peacetime payoff of Project Apollo defies accounting. The mammoth rockets and the colossal engines required to boost huge payloads to high velocity are pieces of hardware that not even a supersalesman can sell in a civilian market. And the scientific data returned from the moon are so esoteric as to be of great value to relatively few scientists. From 1963 through 1972, the United States spent $44.8 billion on NASA-funded space programs. Future funding should be more in line with the demonstrable value of space activity to man's life on earth.

This is not to say that the vast expenditure of public funds for space activity has not had some civilian benefits— or, as NASA experts put it, some technological fallout. I believe that it is beyond the ingenuity of any federal agency to spend $44.8 billion in ten years and not produce *something* of value. But it is a question of *return on the investment.* I happen to believe that automated instruments placed in orbit have great potential in the field of communications and earth-surface reconnaissance—for example, weather investigations, resource surveys, and navigation—but such devices need not be massive and can be propelled into orbit at modest cost. Yet NASA is now set on a manned space program that would entail development of a space earth-to-orbit shuttle and a $50 billion space program for 1978–90 from which the economic payoff would be minimal.

The U.S. atomic program, which has been predominantly military, is rather modest in cost compared with the defense

144

and space programs, yet it has had the greatest peacetime payoff. This is because the AEC has concentrated its civilian efforts on energy-resource development, a matter of vital importance to an industrial society.

If we subtract defense, space, and part of the AEC funds from the U.S. expenditures for science and technology, or discount them heavily as having relatively small civilian pay-off, what we are left with is small compared with R & D funds spent by the private sector of the economy. U.S. companies that divert corporate funds to research and development are seeking a *return* on their investment. This operation is, in effect, supervised by stockholders, who understand that taking funds from profits is potentially risky, but who know from past experience that R & D investments pay off in new products and techniques that bring more profits. Thus R & D-based corporations are esteemed by investors as "growth" companies (Fig. 6-4).

Of course, one might argue that Congress as watchdog of the nation's welfare could be looked upon as the body overseeing research and development and making sure that the public money is not wasted. But such an assumption makes two fundamental assumptions: one, that members of Congress are competent to act as overseers, and two, that they would be objective and not act out of self-interest. Few members of Congress can claim any competence in science and technology. Here the democratic system has broken down because scientists and engineers are not represented in Congress. Moreover, there are even fewer congressmen in committee chairs who lay claim to technical proficiency. Too often the senior members of powerful committees promote R & D projects that bring financial benefits to their own states and districts. Science and technology are such a recent additive to national affairs that Congress has not reformed its traditional ways to accommodate the demands of the innovation. True, it has given indications of reform by establishing specialized committees to deal with atomic energy, space, and other technical topics, but these committees operate in the traditional manner and often promote ventures even though the weight of scientific opinion is evidenced against them.

It is impossible to plot a true curve reflecting the R & D payoffs for the civilian market, but I have sketched in a dotted curve to indicate what I think it is. This curve becomes significant if we compare the R & D expenditures of the United States with those of a country like Japan or Germany, where defense-space expenditures are relatively

FIGURE 6-4

U.S. RESEARCH AND DEVELOPMENT FUNDS (1953–71)

The bottom line represents the growth of expenditures for research and development by U.S. private industries. The middle solid line, which combines private and federal expenditures, shows about the same rate of growth. The top curve, representing total R & D expenditures, includes funds spent by universities, foundations, and other nonprofit institutions. Reckon in constant 1966 dollars (top dotted line), the curve for the total peaks in 1967–68 and is headed downward. (For the sake of simplicity, the 1966-dollar curve is shown for the 1966–71 period only. But, obviously, if that monetary unit were used for the whole chart, the total curve would be raised at the left: the 1953 data point would be $7 billion.) The lower dotted line represents the author's estimate of the growth of total R & D funds spent on projects that are of benefit to the general economy.

FIGURE 6-4

U.S. RESEARCH AND DEVELOPMENT FUNDS
(1953–71)

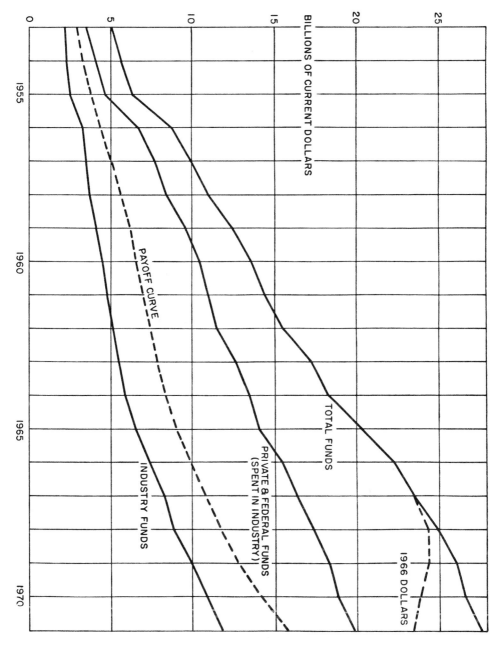

small and where brainpower is focused on areas vital to the economy. If we accept this sketchy curve as approximately correct, then the United States is currently spending 1.6 percent of its gross national product on productive research and development, rather than 2.7 percent, the official figure.

The National Science Foundation has made a 1980 projection of U.S. research-and-development spending, based on continuation of the present 2.7 percent R & D/GNP ratio. The NSF estimate places 1980 R & D spending at between $35 billion and $40 billion (1969 dollars), whereas on our "payoff curve" it would be only $23 billion. I distrust the NSF projection because it fails to take into account the inflated nature of R & D spending, which pumps federal funds into projects having very little boosting effect on the gross national product. Sooner or later, I believe, the U.S. government must take a cold-eyed look at its R & D spending and calculate its potential payoff in much the same way that industrial firms reckon their probable R & D returns.

Here is industry's pattern of R & D funding: it spends its money, first, for electrical equipment and communications gear; second, for chemicals; third, for machinery; and fourth, for motor vehicles and transportation equipment. Almost all of industry's research funds are devoted to development and engineering, but the chemical and metallurgical firms also allocate funds to basic research. No one has ever been able to come up with an adequate definition of basic or fundamental research, but to industry it means research not directly targeted at a specific product or technique. As such, basic research is quite open-ended. Herein lies a difficulty; Congress finds it easy to cut funds for projects and programs that seem to have no direct relation to a public need.

Before World War II, basic research was concentrated in universities and was supported by private funds, often channeled through foundations. When I was a graduate student

at the University of Chicago, a number of researchers conducted cosmic-ray investigations by sending aloft automatic
electronic equipment, much of which was made by slave
labor (i.e., by us graduate students). The equipment was
borne aloft by a long line of latex balloons, which we
launched from Stagg Field and allowed to fly free into the
upper atmosphere. We lacked any telemetry, now common-
place in space flights, so we could only hope that someone
would find the gondola when it descended and notify us.
Finders were offered the munificent sum of ten dollars as a
reward, and I recall that we usually got word promptly. The
point here is that none of us ever dreamed of going to the U.S.
government and soliciting funds for such research. These
were the primitive, but pure, days of high-energy research.

The A-bomb did more than explode with unprecedented
violence; it blasted science into the halls of Congress. Here
was a spectacular development that grew from an intellectual
exercise in the brain of Albert Einstein. The great physicist
carried out his solo endeavors in relating mass and energy
just after the turn of the century, and they seemed utterly
without significance to the practical world. Yet this isolated
bit of basic research was to have a most profound impact on
society.

Congress has valued science for its technological fruits,
and most of the postwar funds for government research and
development have been appropriated for national security
and for matching the Soviets in space-defense technology.
However, scientists have managed to sneak in a few fundamental research projects, so that by 1971 the National
Science Foundation was able to tabulate the following allocation of federal funds for basic research. This tabulation greatly
understates the federal funds channeled into astronomical
sciences, especially if we include planetary science. But, given
the formidable contributions of chemistry to our national economy, chemical sciences are badly skimped in the nation's
basic-research accounts.

Life sciences	$ 578 million
Physics	420
Astronomy	269
Engineering	201
Atmospheric sciences	196
Geological sciences	142
Chemistry	132
Social sciences	91
Oceanography	61
Psychology	61
Mathematics	56
	$2,207 million

One area of research to blossom under the federal fiscal sun has been high-energy physics—the making of huge machines to accelerate atomic particles to very high energy and using them to study the fundamental structure of the inner atom. The Atomic Energy Commission assumed responsibility for funding this field of science, although it has very little practical relationship to atomic energy. In the first three years of the 1970s the AEC spent $640 million on building and operating these big machines. The fundamental investigations carried out with them delight the physicist, but financing them must be reckoned as an act of faith on the part of Congress. Perhaps the only reason congressional funds are provided is that there is an international competition on to build ever-bigger machines to probe still deeper into the crevices of the mysterious nucleus. It is true that research with high-energy machines has added to man's store of knowledge about the universe, but despite the large sums of money diverted to this field in the past quarter-century, the "payoff" for society has been minimal. Certainly, the AEC has never offered any evidence that the big machines can produce nuclear power—which is the main mission of the agency. It is unfortunate that the AEC spends so much on high-energy physics and so relatively little on fusion research, which is the best hope for increasing man's energy sources.

There is very little sense of order or rating of priorities in the House of Science. This is due to the lack of community and organization in the field; there is no overall structure in research activity. Physicists, the glamor boys of World War II, have also been the dominant group since, and their leadership has molded the fortunes of basic science. Only in very recent years have a few scientists questioned the direction of their discipline and attempted to relate scientific activity to human needs. This rebellion against the established order is due in part to a general concern for the environment and in part to the emergence in America of the antitechnology movement. Technologists were held to be guilty of allowing, if not fostering, the pollution of the planet, and a variety of "anti" groups, including conservationists, have advocated a policy of limiting technological growth. The antitechnology movement strikes at the very base of the nation's commitment to science. The average layman makes little distinction between science and technology, so efforts to curb the national technological advance could inflict serious harm on science itself.

The turndown in total R & D funds as described in 1966 dollars (Fig. 6-4) could in the long run have drastic consequences for the progress of science in the United States. Congressmen find it politically painless to cut funds for pure science, since the constituency affected is not numerically large and lacks political clout. Furthermore, the scientific community's inability or reluctance to reform itself makes it vulnerable to public criticism. The danger lies in the distinct possibility that the United States will fail to till the soil of basic research and thus jeopardize its future fertility.

Something of the fertility of the science soil can be gained by studying the rate at which scientific publications, the product of research, have built up since the beginning of the century (Fig. 6-5). The sheer magnitude of the annual production of new titles on chemistry, let alone the mountain of information contained in published papers of earlier years, would seem to challenge the concept of the "availability" of this knowledge. And the problem of coping with scientific information is even more staggering when we add to chemistry all the papers published in other fields of science.

The Atomic Energy Commission began publication of *Nuclear Science Abstracts* in 1948, referencing all scientific articles pertaining to nuclear science (Fig. 6-6). The nuclear literature grew swiftly, in fact even more rapidly than illustrated, because classified reports are not included in *Abstracts*. The AEC practiced rather restrictive security policies and curtailed free publication of technical information in the

FIGURE 6-5

THE GROWTH OF CHEMICAL KNOWLEDGE

The rapid growth of the publication of articles on new findings in chemistry, as tabulated by *Chemical Abstracts*, was truncated by World War I. Between the wars, the growth rate reached a fivefold multiplication before skidding again during World War II. The steady increase in the number of scientific papers on chemistry in the past quarter-century averages 9 percent annually. The annual publication of a quarter million titles in chemistry, a field not flooded with federal funds, is only partially attributable to American scientific activity; about 70 percent of the papers tabulated originate outside the United States. The upper curve represents the total available stockpile of chemical information—almost 50 million scientific papers.

FIGURE 6-5

THE GROWTH OF CHEMICAL KNOWLEDGE

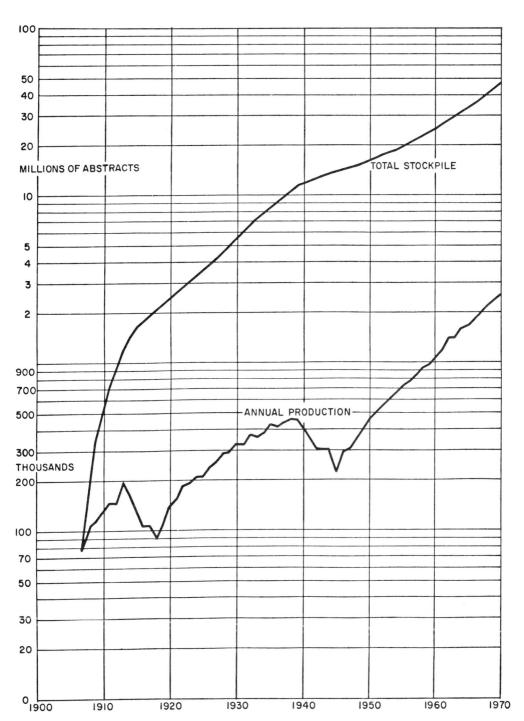

1951–55 period, accounting in part for the plateau in the curve. After 1955 the AEC pursued a more enlightened publications policy and at the same time devoted more effort to the nonmilitary (freely publishable) aspects of atomic energy.

A further illustration of the proliferation of scientific literature is the number of articles indexed in the *High Energy Physics Index,* a rather specialized publication. In 1970 almost ten thousand literature references were detailed by

FIGURE 6-6

POSTWAR GROWTH OF NUCLEAR LITERATURE

Since 1948, the volume of scientific articles on nuclear physics has grown rapidly. In the last two decades, the AEC has abstracted more than half a million scientific reports on the atom.

FIGURE 6-6

POSTWAR GROWTH OF NUCLEAR LITERATURE

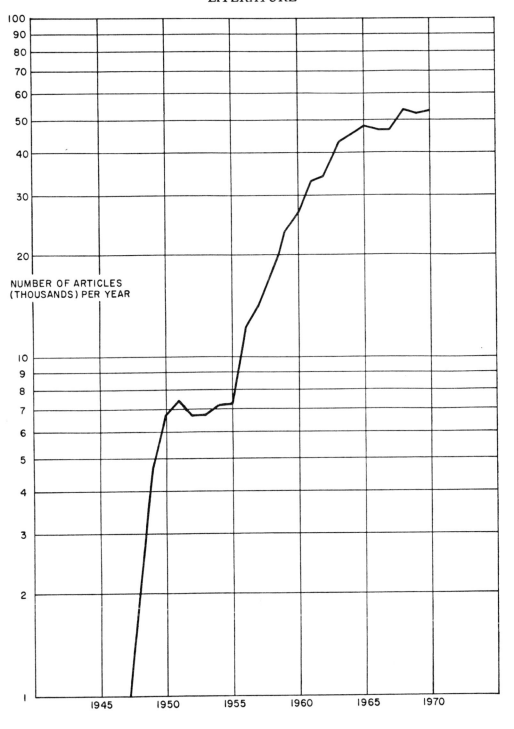

this source, an indication of the degree of specialization that characterizes modern science, tending to bury the individual researcher ever deeper in the crevice of his particular field of interest. This can be a splintering process that develops a superexpert who may know very little about things outside his own specialty. There is a double danger here for society—the expert may prefer the comfort of his own research niche and fail to interest himself in larger issues. He may know all there is to know about the specific toxicity of a pesticide, but neglect to relate its hazard potential to society's vulnerability. Or he may be willing to emerge from his crevice to take action on a public issue, but lack the ability to act wisely.

This issue of the public responsibility of the scientist is a grave one in a society buffeted by wave after wave of new technological developments. The scientist himself is hard put to stay afloat in the rising sea. Scientist-historian Derek J. de Solla Price has studied the growth in the numbers of scientific journals published over the course of almost three centuries (Fig. 6-7). As he points out: "In the course of this proliferation of the scientific journals, it became evident that by about 1830 the process had reached a point of absurdity: no scientist could read all the journals or keep sufficiently conversant with all published work that might be relevant to his interest." It was at this point that the abstract journal was invented—an index-summary of the current literature that allowed a scientist to select articles rather than plow through a vast melange of print.

Today even the number of abstract journals bulks large, and some twentieth-century invention was needed to deal with the proliferation. A new field of information science has sprung up with the development of the computer as a tool for handling data acquisition and retrieval on a large scale. Dr. Eugene Garfield, president of the Institute for Scientific Information, has called this containment "the information implosion." Although there are tens of thousands of scientific journals, Dr. Garfield points out: "Studies made by ISI indicate that fewer than 1,000 journals account for over 90% of the significant scientific reports." Even a thousand journals are still too many for the individual to scan, and it is here that computers come in. Organizations like Garfield's process information from more than two thousand scientific journals and store it in a computer memory bank. Not only is the article itself indexed, all its literature citations are also recorded. In 1971 a five-year cumulative *Science Citation Index* was published in which a total of 9 million entries were printed. This, in itself, might seem a bit unwieldy, but it is available on magnetic tape and a researcher may ask for very specific data and have an answer read out in short order.

Many of the large number of chemical reports deal with new chemical compounds. As many as two hundred thousand of these may come to light in a single year. Again, this mass of technical data would seem intractable, but it can also be computerized and systematically itemized, as in *Current Abstracts of Chemistry and Index Chemicus.*

As a scientist who has strayed from the field of pure physics to the study of defense science, I myself sometimes feel the weight of massed data. For example, six volumes of defense appropriations hearings of the House of Representatives add up to 6,776 pages of fine print for fiscal 1972. And this represents the output of a single congressional committee; there are four in all that deal with national-defense problems. Unfortunately, there is no computerized access to this bulky set of volumes.

Because of the high level of intelligence required for the generation of new scientific information, a modern society is in a sense dependent for progress on the right-hand tip of the I.Q. curve. As will be recalled, this is a single-humped (bell) curve peaking at 100. Below 70 on the left-hand side of the hump we find the intellectually deprived, the morons, and still farther to the left as the curve drops to zero, the imbeciles and the idiots. The average high school graduate has an I.Q. that peaks just above 110, and the college-graduate curve is humped just below 120. Ph.D.'s have an average I.Q. of 135, with a few as low as 100; and others, the very gifted, have an I.Q. exceeding 160. The intellectually gifted, when they also possess drive and creativity, can form the cutting edge of modern science and technology.

As we now turn to analysis of the factors limiting growth in the twentieth century, we will inevitably encounter more examples of the misuse and abuse of technology. But the answer is not to head in the direction of less technology;

FIGURE 6-7

THREE CENTURIES OF SCIENTIFIC JOURNALS

The number of scientific journals has grown precipitously during the past three centuries. By 1830 it became evident that no one man could hope to keep up with them all, and the abstract journal was invented. The new kind of publication was an index and a brief summary of articles published in a given scientific field.

158

FIGURE 6-7

THREE CENTURIES OF SCIENTIFIC JOURNALS

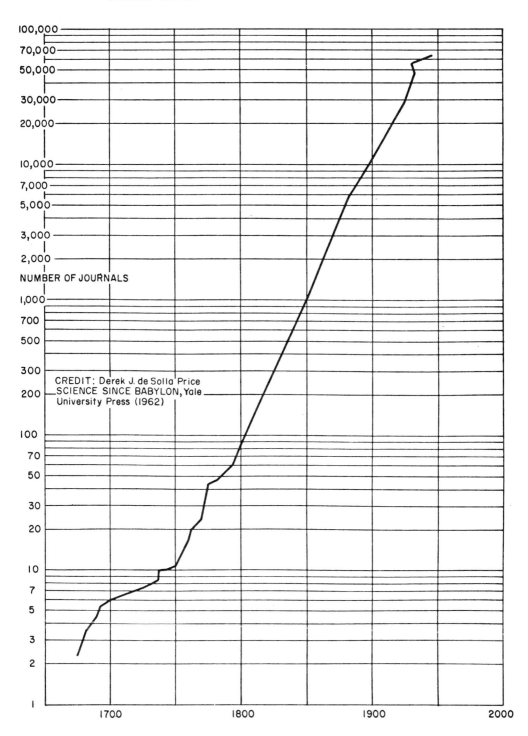

CREDIT: Derek J. de Solla Price
SCIENCE SINCE BABYLON, Yale
University Press (1962)

NUMBER OF JOURNALS

national therapy to repair the rape and ruin of the environment will require the concentrated concern of our most
skilled citizens. What we need is not less technology but a
new compass heading to steer a course toward bringing men
into balance with his resources and environment. One such
direction must surely be an arresting of growth both in population and in per capita consumption.

CHAPTER

7

THE QUESTION OF GROWTH

We have previously more or less exonerated past population growth as the primary cause of the excesses illustrated by our semi-log charts. It is per capita consumption that has increased so precipitously in the past seventy years, and, measured against that, the more sluggish increase in U.S. population has had a minor effect on total consumption. But because no abatement of the high levels of per capita consumption seems imminent, the population growth of the future becomes a major consideration.

We have noted (Fig. 1-3) that the 1970 U.S. population was 204 million, or twice what it was in 1920. This fifty-year doubling time is lengthening, fortunately, and if, from now on, two children on an average were born to each couple, in about half a century (2020) the U.S. population would equal 300 million. About two children per family represents a steady state (one in which the species just reproduces itself), and that would be attained late in the twenty-first century

(Fig. 7-1). If all families restricted themselves to 2 children, this would not suddenly level out the population curve because there are increasing numbers of women who will become of child-bearing age in the future. Future population depends not only on the fertility rate, but also on the number of women who reach child-bearing age.

If, on the other hand, each family had three children, then the U.S. population figures would soar, reaching 400 million within half a century, and would double again in the

FIGURE 7-1

U.S. POPULATION PROJECTIONS (1870–2070)

If, from now on, each couple in America were to have an average of two children, the present population of 204 million would grow to 300 million less than fifty years from now—in 2020 (lower dotted line). The growth curve would reach a plateau a century hence. If the average per couple were *three* children, the growth curve would take off into the stratosphere (upper dotted line). The population would double by 2020, double again by 2050, and exceed a billion by 2080.

FIGURE 7-1

U.S. POPULATION PROJECTIONS (1870–2070)

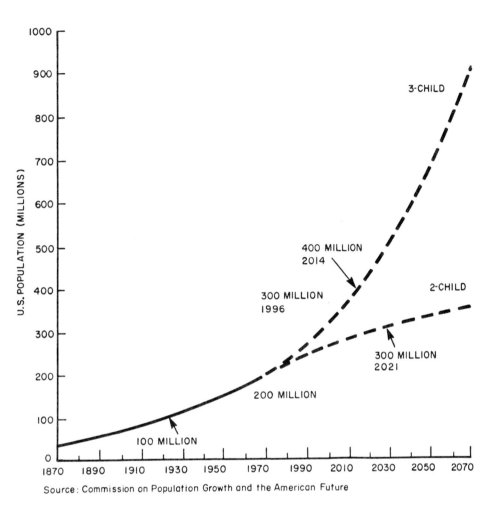

Source: Commission on Population Growth and the American Future

middle of the twenty-first century; by the year 2080 there would be more than a billion U.S. citizens. The U.S. Commission on Population Growth and the American Future has observed:

> Our past rapid growth has given us so many young couples that they would have to limit their child-bearing to an average of only about one child to produce the number of births consistent with immediate zero growth. Ten years from now, the population under 10 years old would only be 43% of what it now is, with disruptive effects on the school system and ultimately on the number of persons entering the labor force. Thereafter, a constant total population could be maintained only if this small generation in turn had two children and their grandchildren had nearly three children on the average. And then the process would again have to reverse, so that the overall effect for many years would be that of an accordion-like mechanism requiring continuous expansion and contraction.

Viewed graphically, the commission's picture of zero population growth is a snakelike series of oscillations averaging around a constant level. In the rest of this book we shall make the assumption, optimistic perhaps, that the U.S. population will no more than double in the next hundred years. The technical means of easy contraception are now available for the female, and soon will be for the male; the United States will be able to provide the mechanism for controlling population growth, if a national policy to that end is adopted.

The question is, Will the future growth of energy in the United States match the increased demand of a growing population? Our year-2000 projection of total energy consumption in the United States is the energy equivalent of 33 billion barrels of oil. That is 120 barrels of oil per person for our year-2000 population of 280 million. But we have estimated that the actual consumption of oil at the end of the

164

century will range from 11 to 15 billion barrels per year. The median, 13 billion barrels, is two and a half times as much as present consumption. Besides allowing for population growth, this estimate projects a factor of 1.8 increase in the oil consumption per capita. If people in the United States consume no more oil in the year 2000 than now, reckoned on a per capita basis, then the total oil consumption would be 7.2 billion barrels per year.

Present usage of oil as an energy fuel accounts for nine-tenths of its consumption, distributed among sectors of the economy as follows:

Transportation	61%
Household and commercial	23
Industrial	11
Electric utilities	4

This is quite different from the use of oil in Japan, for example, where most of it is consumed in utility plants and in domiciles. It would be very convenient if one could set down the U.S.A. sector use of oil in the year 2000, but any such projection would rest on many assumptions about the price of oil relative to competitive fuels and about government policy regarding oil imports, the availability of synthetic oil, and, most important, the transportation mix of the United States. If, for example, it becomes federal policy to abandon lavish support of the federal highway system or to regulate the horsepower of Detroit's new models or to clamp on a federal tax designed to discourage the use of motor fuel, the demand on the market would be reduced. (The present four-cents-per-gallon federal tax on gasoline is not much of a deterrent nor is it meant to be, but even the addition of five to nine cents a gallon in state taxes would not constitute a prohibitive price for American motorists.)

What would it take in the way of gasoline taxes to discourage motor-fuel consumption? The cost of operating a fairly new motor vehicle is from twelve to fourteen cents per mile, of which the fuel cost varies from one to four cents for cars ranging from Volkswagens to Cadillacs. Forcing the motorist to pay more than fifty cents a gallon may enrage most people, but I doubt that it will cool down America's protracted love affair with the automobile. More and more people might ask the new-car salesman, "How many miles per gallon?" but then people would probably grumble and snarl at the gas station attendants and go on buying gas. Before inquiring into such restrictive measures, we need to ask, why impose such taxes at all? What is the basic reason for trying to reduce oil consumption?

Although the federal standards for automotive emissions have yet to be met by auto manufacturers (1975 is the deadline), it is reasonable to assume that by the 1980s the pollution problem caused by the internal-combustion engine will be under control. This may require official restrictions on horsepower, but atmospheric pollution due to motor traffic will probably not bring about a reduction in the use of petroleum. However, unless the synthetic fuels come on stream in unexpectedly large volumes by the 1980s—and there is little reason to believe they will—the U.S. demand for oil will have to be met by imports. In 1971, when the international oil companies negotiated with the oil-producing nations of the Middle East, they got a small sample of the menu that the Persian Gulf proffered and it was not a tasty morsel. Clearly, the drift of the United States toward greater dependence on oil from the Persian Gulf will put it more and more at the mercy of the oil sheiks. The United States will have to look elsewhere for energy security—for a source of energy that it can rely on for the future. Planning for the future with the oil sheiks in command is hardly a creditable posture for the United States, especially in the face of energy needs that mount steadily every year.

An industry organization, the Oil Companies of America, took note of the situation in 1971 and ran an ad in *The*

New York Times headlined "Better check your oil. You're using 614,000 barrels an hour," and predicted, "Perhaps as early as 1985, we'll be using one million barrels an hour." That's 8.7 billion barrels a year. Where will it come from? The oil companies said, "The best way, we think, is to find more oil." But the cliché is far from a solution, and no facts have turned up to modify the prediction that this nation will soon confront a true oil crisis. The reason for the United States to consider moderating its oil demands is that the oil barrel is running dry, and no domestic sources offer the prospect of refilling it or of keeping pace with demands. Thus the lack of adequate domestic reserves, the uncertainty about available synthetics, and the perilous overseas supply combine to argue for a conservation of petroleum, which means restrictions on the use of gasoline for transportation.

Assuming that the U.S. government adopts a policy of conserving petroleum, how should it be put into effect? There is the bulldozer approach: arbitrarily set a belt-tightening national objective of, say, 7 billion barrels of petroleum for the year 2000, then plan to supply this from a source mix of 1 Bb from the contiguous forty-eight states, 1 Bb from Alaska and offshore oil, and 2 Bb from conversion of mined solids (coal, oil shale, and tar sands) for a total of 4 Bb (57%) directly under U.S. control, leaving 3 Bb to be supplied by imports. The United States could use the lever of domestic synthetic oil to prevent price gouging by the Middle East. Assuming that it would be politically possible to lay down and implement such a plan, the big problem would be making out such a restrictive oil budget for the nation. Disregarding the unknowns for a moment, let us make the brute-force assumption that by the year 2000 half the oil budget will be set aside for transportation. This would be about 50 percent more motor fuel than is now used, but less than the estimated 1990 consumption (Chapter 2).

Any assessment of oil in the nation's future must deal with the facts about the distribution of our population and the transportation requirements the existing pattern imposes (Fig. 7-2). One-fifth of all Americans—a total of 42 million —live in about 0.1 percent of the total U.S. area, corresponding to the area of Rhode Island and Delaware. More than half the U.S. population lives in fewer than one hundred metropolitan areas.

FIGURE 7-2

U.S. POPULATION DEPLOYMENT (1970)

About two-thirds of all Americans live on a land area that is less than 1 percent of the country's total. This chart differs from the preceding ones in that both its horizontal and its vertical scales are logarithmic, making it log-log instead of semi-log.

FIGURE 7-2

U.S. POPULATION DEPLOYMENT (1970)

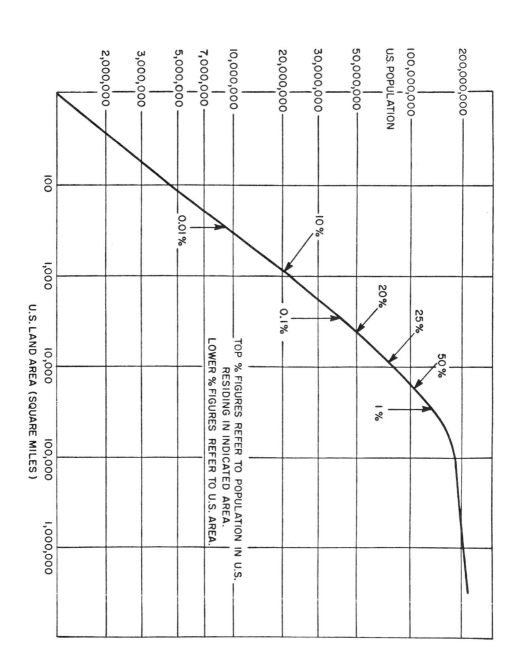

Data obtained from the 1970 census are given in Table 7-1 and show just how metropolitan Americans have become.

TABLE 7-1

Urban Places Greater than	Number	Population—1970
1,000,000 population	6	18,742 million
500,000	20	12,967
250,000	30	10,442
100,000	100	14,285
Totals	156	56,436 million

At first glance it might appear that the condensation of people into a relatively small area of the U.S. land mass would simplify the transportation problem. But the automobile has promoted a massive suburban sprawl. From the farthest tentacles of which some workers commute as much as 100 miles, one way, each day.

The statistics displayed in Table 7-1 do not adequately represent the population distribution in the United States because the heading "urban places" has limited meaning. If we look on another page of the *U.S. Statistical Abstract* we find the metropolitan area populations, truer indices of the problem we will address, as shown in Table 7-2.

TABLE 7-2

Metropolitan Areas Greater than	Number	Population—1970
1,000,000 population	27	68,681 million
500,000	31	21,113
250,000	39	13,657
Totals	97	103,451 million

Here we see that half the U.S. population concentrates in fewer than one hundred metropolitan areas; these are the industrial ganglia in the U.S. economic nervous system, and their day-to-day functioning is essential to our national well-being. These centers are also the great energy consumers, and a most vital component of this energy is the flow of premium fuels which allows people and things to be transported within the metropolitan areas and, of course, from one to another. The majority of the labor force concentrates in these relatively few areas, and a continuous flow of gasoline must be maintained to keep workers on the job and to maintain the orderly operation of the huge communities.

The U.S. government has attempted to ease the worker's commutation woes by a vast infusion of federal highway funds and by building peripheral highways, and as a result it has underfunded mass-transit systems and perpetuated a system of individual transportation that takes a high toll of U.S. fuel reserves. Of course, the United States could resort to the World War II expedient of gas rationing, but this is not likely to be a politically popular measure. Nor can the government legislate the establishment of car pools or require multiple occupancy of all vehicles. An escalating horsepower tax, with higher fees for engines rated at more than 150 hp, could dampen Detroit's zeal for marketing even-larger engines. Strictly speaking, we should specify a restriction on cubic inches of displacement in the piston cylinder, but this concept is less real to most people.

Cutting back on superpowered motor cars when the total road mileage reaches the 2-trillion-mile mark could conserve 1 billion, and possibly 2 billion, barrels of gasoline a year. This would mean mothballing the 2-ton Cadillacs, but it would keep the United States mobile somewhat longer. At the same time, a concerted drive to provide attractive modes of mass transportation could cut back the 2 trillion miles of passenger travel postulated for the future and thus bring the petroleum demand within more reasonable limits. Whether or not such a national policy could be adopted de-

171

pends upon the will of Congress or, ultimately, of the people, and the people cannot be expected to support restrictive measures unless they are persuaded of their necessity. An energy crisis does impend, but I suspect that few Americans know it. The president's energy message of June 1971 implied a future energy crisis but did little to document it.

Meeting the fuel crisis in transportation will require planning a suitable supply-demand structure for all uses of petroleum, not just dividing up the oil barrel into fractions for cars, planes, diesel trucks, trains, and boats, but for stationary consumption of petroleum as well. Industrial lubricants, utility-plant residual oil, home-heating distillates, and additional refinery products are required in every metropolitan area. U.S. cities are highly dynamic organisms that must be kept fueled.

U.S. refineries are tuned to the maximum production of higher distillates, like gasoline—the most profitable products. Gasoline's cut of the oil barrel is 43 percent, while there is almost no production of unprofitable lower distillates like residual oil, which is in great demand by East Coast electric plants. A change in oil policy dictating a shift in distillery output would require substantial adjustments by the refineries. The decision to reduce the lead content of gasoline caused refiners to switch to higher distillates to supply higher-octane gasoline. Ironically, the decision that caused automobile manufacturers to lower the compression ratio of high-performance engines so that unleaded gas could be used also meant that the engines consumed more gasoline. Thus an antipollution measure imposed a further demand upon the nation's oil supply.

In recent years urban transportation systems have come under intensive study. The majority of households with an annual income of less than three thousand dollars do not own cars, but most of the rest do, and they have increasingly moved out from the city to the suburbs and acquired the commuting habit. Unfortunately, urban geography, the high cost of new roads, and the inability or unwillingness of suburban communities to build access highways combine to produce a diurnal traffic strangulation. In most U.S. cities the traffic tide is a one-way flood; in San Francisco, for example, vehicular traffic is inbound in the morning and outbound at night, meaning that mass-transit vehicles make near-empty return trips or simply park at the end of the line to wait for the next traffic surge. This is a highly inefficient use of a transit system, yet people who do not own cars, who could patronize the system and fill the empty seats, cannot find jobs at the suburban places easily reached by the system.

Public hopes for traffic relief are periodically raised by news releases about some fancy experimental high-speed surface system, such as the TACV (Tracked Air Cushion Vehicle) boasting speeds of up to 300 miles per hour. But the real problem is to move people in large numbers at dependable speeds of around 30 miles per hour; most commuters would be overjoyed by such "speed" if it could be relied upon every day.

There is grave danger that the United States will simply drift into a fuel crisis through failure to apply restraints on Detroit's monomania for high-powered road locomotives, and then extreme measures will have to be taken. The stoppage of the vital energy fluid, oil, to a city like New York is tantamount to a metropolitan coronary. Federal authorities planning transportation systems must incorporate fuel controls into their programs. At present most agencies of government are proceeding on the assumption that the fuel lines of America will always be full; they are blind to the dimensions of the oil crisis that impends. Meanwhile demand escalates. Any steps we take now to increase future energy supplies must be highly productive ones, otherwise they may not be worth taking at all. The magnitude of the demand and the rate at which it is increasing will defeat any small-scale and laggardly approaches.

If the nation's mobility creates a complex problem in energy planning, the fueling of stationary energy plants is an even tougher one because of the even more rapid rate of fuel consumption for electric power and because the new technologies engender novel pollution problems. A number of very vocal environmentalists have particularly opposed the building of more nuclear-electric generating plants. In Eugene, Oregon, the proposed construction of a nuclear-power station was put to a public vote and rejected. Many citizens who fought against it did so because they wished to preserve the small-town character of Eugene. To be sure, other arguments were used against the installation, but the antigrowth sentiment was very strong in the community. This, of course, is a case for local option—if a community wishes to refrain from growth, that is for it to decide. But if a *nation* deliberately decides to flatten out its energy curve, then it must be prepared to accept the consequences and buffer its economy against the adverse effects of the limitation.

A nation, like a cell, is an organism that cannot function without energy and cannot grow without increasing its use of energy. The advocates of "zero growth" would restrict increases in the nation's electric capacity to protect the environment and restore the purity of the air and the water. They argue that we have progressed far enough, that it is time to call a halt. But these "plateau people" do not tell us how to deal with the economic, political, and social consequences of zero growth. They do present a list of objections, including thermal pollution, contested land use, radioactive effluent hazards, reactor safety, and aesthetic damage.

Certainly the United States can trim its energy needs by practicing more conservative policies and avoiding needless or wasteful use of energy. Indeed, the Office of Emergency Planning authored a 1972 publication of some 238 pages, brimful with ideas for cutting back energy consumption. The agency of the White House estimated that a 16 percent reduction in energy could be accomplished by 1980 and as much as 25 percent by 1990. But, by the latter date, the OEP report estimated energy consumption would be twice that of 1971 if the United States did not adopt a strict energy diet. Since the OEP report did not spell out how the United States would bring about energy conservation, the estimates must be regarded as theoretical goals. Even if the goals were achieved, the actual total energy requirement for 1990, for example, still imposes a heavy burden on sources of supply and certainly overburdens domestic premium fuel reserves.

Environmentalists have real cause for their fear that uncontrolled expansion of electric capacity would be damaging, and their crusading has undoubtedly accelerated the application of controls to the siting and design of new power plants. The most potent of these is the National Environmental Policy Act (NEPA) and, in particular, the Section 102 requirement that federal agencies file statements with the Council on Environmental Quality detailing the environmental impact of potentially injurious construction activities and operations. The requirements of the Water Quality Improvement Act and other acts of Congress are further brakes on the potentially detrimental effects of stationary power sources. The Environmental Protection Agency has also formulated standards that the various states have adopted for controlling thermal pollution. For example, the water use by steam-electric plants had to be curtailed for the simple reason that the historic trend indicates that a sustained use of cooling water would preempt too much of the available supply (Fig. 5-6). However, many utilities are scheduling cooling towers or lakes for treatment of plant water, and it seems realistic to project a water use of 200 billion gallons per day by steam-electric plants in the year 2000—only twice that of 1960, despite a more than tenfold increase in electric-energy production. (We exclude estimates on the use of sea water for cooling, since it is not resource limited.) Thus, it seems clear that proper planning and enforcement of controls can bring thermal pollution from power generation into a manageable framework.

The generation and distribution of power preempt considerable areas of land and become a factor in aesthetic or visual pollution. However, until underground transmission of electric power becomes feasible on a large scale, the number of transmission towers is bound to increase. Sometimes it is harder to secure rights-of-way for transmission lines than it is to find a suitable power-generation site. Shorter transmission lines would minimize the slicing of access corridors through the country, but these would mean building plants closer to cities and would thus enhance the risk of the routine or accidental release of effluents to larger populations. The trend toward putting nuclear-power plants onshore or just offshore minimizes the thermal-pollution hazard in most cases, but this is obviously no aid to inland cities unless power can be sent over long lines. Should the energy potential of the low-sulfur and abundant subbituminous coal in Montana and Wyoming be exploited for the production of electricity, then a new system of long-line transmission will be devised to feed the power to the energy-hungry Midwest.

The routine release of effluents from steam-electric plants is a problem that opponents of nuclear plants have seized upon as part of a national antinuclear campaign. The whole issue was badly framed for the public, which was all too prone to equate a power reactor with an A-bomb. However, in mid-1971, when the Atomic Energy Commission issued its more stringent guidelines for radiation standards for nuclear-power plants, it went a long way toward defusing the radioactive-effluent issue. Then the independent appraisal of the Environmental Protection Agency tended to take the AEC off the hook. And the excessive pollution caused by the Four Corners fossil-fueled electric stations made it clear that all effluents, both chemical and radioactive, should be considered in assessing power-plant hazards. The new AEC rules for effluent releases and the surveillance of the nuclear sites by independent groups should reassure the public that the general health is being protected.

As for the matter of nuclear safety, the issue is far from resolved for water reactors. (See Chapter 4.) Coastal siting, where several miles of water isolate the reactor from land, provides a margin of safety, for it is in this inner zone that the most hazardous radioactivity would be likely to fall out in the event of an accident.

The aesthetics of industrial construction are highly subjective, but modern nuclear-electric plants are certainly less unsightly than fossil-fueled units, especially coal-fired types that entail huge coal yards, tall smokestacks, and noxious effluents. If society demands energy, then it must pay a price, because there is no such thing as zero-impact generation and distribution of energy.

In its headlong pursuit of cheap power, the United States has in the past neglected even to reckon the costs. Now that it is compelled to deal with uncertain fossil-fuel availability and such hazards as strip-mining, along with pollution problems, the nation is in the process of lurching away from dirty to clean energy. As might be expected when forces of reaction set in, extremists argue against the slightest actual or conjectured environmental impact, and nuclear power has been attacked as something of a national villain.

The desirability of growth, as such, is clearly challengeable in the case of America's mobile-power sources, on the bases of both pollution and resource limitation. However, in the case of stationary power sources, pollution alone is indicted, but unless the fossil-fuel effluents are regarded as impossible to control, the antigrowth advocates have to make a more substantial case. It is simply not sufficient to contest growth of power capacity without pinpointing the specific injury inflicted, beyond hope of prevention or remedy, by the electric station. Now that the federal and state governments have the authority to control the power situation, its expansion must be challenged on specific grounds. The Skelly Wright decision of July 1971 forced the Atomic Energy Commission to make an in-depth assessment of the environmental impact of a nuclear installation, and the AEC, in deciding not to appeal the decision, indicated it would make thorough evaluations of specific nuclear sites and plants before granting construction permits and operating licenses. These environmental-impact statements are accessible, and intervenors or interested parties will be in a position to judge whether their interests are being safeguarded.

Assuming then that the mechanism exists for objective evaluation of power-plant hazards and for intervention in the event of doubt about such assessments, a community that wishes to rule out the siting of a stationary power source nearby must make a decision reflecting the consensus of its citizens. A community that denies itself energy sources must, in the end, come to grips with the risk-benefit balance of the denial. It is easy to whip up public sentiment in opposition to a potential hazard, but what happens in the same community when the working man learns that lack of energy in the future may cause industry to move elsewhere? It is at this point, when industry threatens to withdraw jobs from a community, that an antigrowth backlash may ensue. For example, in Midland, Michigan, an antinuclear power-plant movement was gaining strength until the Dow Chemical Company hinted that it would move its operations elsewhere. Then Dow's opponents met with vituperative responses from townspeople who feared for their jobs.

The Midland case is a quick-reaction example, since the Dow Chemical Company is a major employer in the area, but in communities where this kind of job threat is less immediate, public response may be delayed until the economic results of a power shortage become evident. Thus the issue must always be fully aired so that residents are aware of both the risks and the benefits. Major power plants take from seven to ten years to bring on line, and a large city that voluntarily denies itself a nearby power site may find, when it awakens to the economic consequences of its act, that many years will be required to close the energy gap.

Growth opponents, especially those championing "zero growth," argue that the electric energy consumed today is excessive and that America could do with far fewer kilowatt-hours. Admittedly, the long U.S. enchantment with cheap power has led to carelessness. At a National Energy Forum held in Washington, D.C., in September 1971, Edwin L. Kennedy, energy expert for Lehman Brothers, observed, "Cheap energy is behind us, but abundant energy need not be." When he spoke, many utilities had just announced stiff rate hikes, some as much as 25 percent. But the effect of such hikes—a temporary lessening in demand—is unlikely to curtail electric-power growth. The evidence suggests that the growth curve given in Figure 3-7 is not going to be far off the mark and that the use of electric energy in the United States will continue its historic trend line until the end of this century.

My opinion is that this curve, too, must bend over as the per capita electric-energy consumption exceeds 30,000 kilowatt-hours per year. My projection infuriates environmentalists, who leap to label me a shill for the utilities, but I have no reason to defend the energy industry. I believe that given the physical ability of the nation to produce power within its resources, and without serious insult to the environment, it is unreasonable to make cutbacks in power generation that could have repressive effects on the economy. I am completely sympathetic with any movement that seeks to make the United States more BTU-conscious, but I am also aware of the realities of power usage in our democracy. Electricity cannot be rationed in any equitable manner unless each household is assigned a monthly quota and a mechanism is installed to monitor the allocation. Such a control-rationing system would not be difficult to devise, but it would be a political nightmare to implement. For example, would the Browns, living next to the air-conditioned Jones family, be granted extra kilowatt-hours when they bought an air conditioner?

Zeroing in on a single household, the author's, let us look at how the Lapp family of four imposed its energy demand on the utilities in 1971. The Virginia Electric and Power Company billed me for $317.00 for 13,560 kilowatt-hours; this included $35.60 in local taxes. I estimate that in order to deliver this electric energy to my home, VEPCO had a central station fuel cost of about 400 million BTUs. To this we must add 212 million BTUs piped to my house on the Potomac just south of Alexandria. The Washington Gas Light Company kindly provided this natural gas for $338.41, of which $31.66 went for local taxes. Thus my 1971 demand on the local utilities amounted to roughly 600 million BTUs.

The natural gas, of course, was burned to provide hot water and to keep the Lapps warm during a rather mild winter. The more versatile kilowatt served a wide variety of end uses in my home, and I have estimated their annual consumption as shown in Table 7-3.

TABLE 7-3

LAPP FAMILY'S HOUSEHOLD BTU CONSUMPTION—1971

Central air conditioner	4,500 kwh
Lighting	2,500
Electric range and oven	1,500
Clothes washer and dryer	1,400
Furnace fan	1,000
Refrigerator	650
Television (2)	600
Dishwasher	500
Radio (2) and hi-fi	350
Typewriter	150
Electric iron	100
Waste disposal	75
Vacuum cleaner	50
Toaster	40
Floor polisher	25
Sun lamp	25
Food mixer/blender	20
Electric shaver	20
Battery charger, tools, clocks, etc.	50
	13,555 kwh

If kilowatt curbs were imposed by some means, how would I cut back my consumption of electricity? First, my consumption is not excessive, since the average VEPCO residential billing is 11,000 kilowatt-hours per year. But this includes apartment dwellers and townhouse residents, who make less demand on utilities. I think that any effort to reduce consumption would focus on the major items. Judging from my total lack of success in getting lights turned out by screaming at the kids, "Turn out the lights . . . you know I'm writing a book about energy," I will not cut back on lighting. The major consumer, air conditioning, is probably the one I would concentrate on, but this would be done at some discomfort.

Barring a switch to electric heating for hot water or for my home, I do not foresee any increase in electric energy use, and I would, in fact, predict a small decrease when the boys go to college. But my household is certainly not representative of all America, since I am near saturation in the population of gadgets that consume energy in my home. But households of the lower income brackets and those belonging to minority groups are far from saturation. As Irwin M. Stelzer, president of National Economics Research Associates, Inc., wrote in 1971: "To adopt a policy which, by a sort of grandfather's clause, would seek to prevent those of lower incomes and darker skins from sharing in the not-inconsiderable comforts and conveniences afforded by modern electric appliances seems to me somewhat illiberal."

If an area were assigned an energy quota, how would it live within it if a manufacturer came to town and offered to build his plant there? Would the community as a whole agree to accept further restrictions in order to allow a new plant to come in? Or what would happen when home builders applied for permits to construct badly needed new housing—construction that would require new wiring? Such are the tough issues that a zero-growth community would face.

From a national viewpoint, the inability to supply new power would deny new productivity gains to industry and commerce, since their output can be increased only by adding electromechanical improvements. A high degree of automation has already occurred in mass-production lines, but similar advances have not characterized much of the service industries. The shoemaker still uses much the same repair machines his father had, and the mailman, although more mobile than his predecessors, has yet to show any increase in productivity. Hand sorting of mail may some day be replaced by electro-optical processes, but it will still take the human eye to decipher handwriting. Yet the service trades constitute an increasing part of the so-called Gross National Product, throwing an added burden on the manufacturing industries to boost their own contribution to the total.

Every time a person buys an air conditioner, or a television set, or any power-consuming gadget for his home, he also imposes an additional BTU demand on the manufacturing sector, that is, the capital cost involved in making the appliance or product. Thus a utility that had the nerve to promote a ban on air conditioner sales would immediately come in conflict with the manufacturers and distributors who are anxious to sell new products. It is significant that awareness of energy consumption by window air conditioners has led to advertising in which certain companies have promoted their products as less energy consuming than competitors' window units. But in general the attempt to curtail consumption through limitation of sales seems downright un-American to most industrialists. The U.S. Department of the Interior appears to favor continued escalation of industrial growth, for it has made breakdowns of industrial use of electric energy as shown in Table 7-4.

TABLE 7-4

	1968	2000	
		Low	High
Food and allied products	36	189	213 billion kwh
Paper and allied products	30	169	192
Chemicals and allied products	173	953	1,078
Petroleum industries	24	132	149
Building materials	30	160	181
Primary metals	138	755	854
Minerals and manufacturing	167	925	1,046
Total Industrial Energy	598	3,283	3,713 billion kwh

This industrial energy growth of nearly sixfold in the last third of the century is fundamental to the plans of U.S. electric utilities.

The electric utilities are classed under services, and they have managed to achieve productivity increases by acting on the slogan "Bigger is better." That is to say, they have turned to economies of scale by building larger and larger plants. The result has been a regular decrease in the cost of the kilowatt-hour, mainly to the benefit of industry and commerce, which together account for two-thirds of U.S. electric-energy consumption. Thus, cutting back on domestic use would not go far toward solving the problem of energy conservation. A wiser national course might be not to cut back, but to increase electric output, especially if providing the nation with adequate fuel eventually makes conservation of fossil fuels mandatory. Then the nuclear-electric program of the United States makes eminent sense and should be supported by conservationists. Moreover, any major shift in the transportation philosophy of the country, for example, from privately owned vehicles to mass-transportation systems, throws a very heavy demand on electric generating capacity.

Putting the two problems of mobile and stationary energy sources into perspective, I believe that the nation's mobility poses the greater challenge for the future. Suppose that either for reasons of controlling pollutants or for reasons of conserving liquid fuel, Detroit is forced to market cars with greatly reduced horsepower, say in the Volkswagen class. If the auto makers are to give the American motorist the performance he is used to, car weight (and size) will have to be reduced. Detroit would have to make only cars in the compact-economy class, abandoning the V-8–propelled medium- and luxury-class models. The impact of such a marketing shift is elucidated in Figure 7-3. All of which means that the current entry item, under the column of national-income accounts, must list the automobile and all its associated services as exceeding $100 billion, or about one dollar in every six and a half of the nation's total business. Forcing Detroit to downgrade its product to light-weight, less-expensive models could send the curves in Figure 7-3 sliding down rather sharply and trigger a turndown in business activity. Automobile makers might conceivably make up their sales by turning to new markets, such as mass-transit vehicles. But the replacement market for those would be comparatively small. In effect, the United States would be converting its motor vehicles to the European style, and the American life-style would have to change accordingly.

FIGURE 7-3

RETAIL SALES AND SERVICES CONNECTED WITH AUTOMOBILES (1933–71)

The dollar value of all retail sales made to motor-vehicle owners—cars, accessories, tires, parts—is represented in the uppermost curve. The lower curve represents gasoline sales. The isolated point below the curves, on the $10 billion line, indicates the amount spent for automotive-repair services in 1971.

FIGURE 7-3

RETAIL SALES AND SERVICES CONNECTED WITH AUTOMOBILES (1933–71)

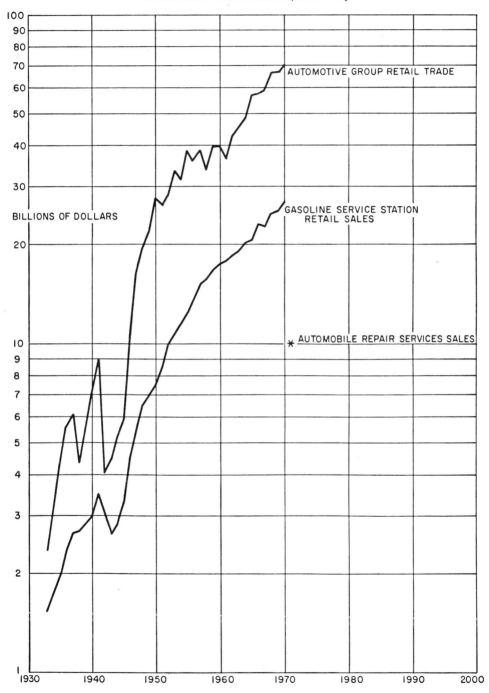

Indeed, Americans in the year 2000 may look back to the days of fuel abundance in mid-century and marvel at the huge four-wheeled chariots of their parents and grandparents.

America's single most critical demand for liquid fuel is for motor gasoline (Fig. 7-4), and jet aircraft demand an increasing volume of naphtha-kerosene fuels. Over 90 percent of gasoline is distilled from crude oil (the rest is processed from condensates and natural-gas liquids), of which

FIGURE 7-4

GASOLINE AND JET FUEL CONSUMPTION
(1916–70) AND PROJECTED DEMAND
(1970–2000)

The 1970 U.S. consumption of gasoline was about
2 billion barrels (42 gallons = 1 barrel). The crude-oil
source requirement, about two barrels of crude for each
barrel of gasoline, is represented at the upper right.
The dotted lines projecting future consumption of both
gasoline and aircraft fuel are based on Department
of the Interior estimates.

FIGURE 7-4

GASOLINE AND JET FUEL CONSUMPTION (1916–70) AND PROJECTED DEMAND (1970–2000)

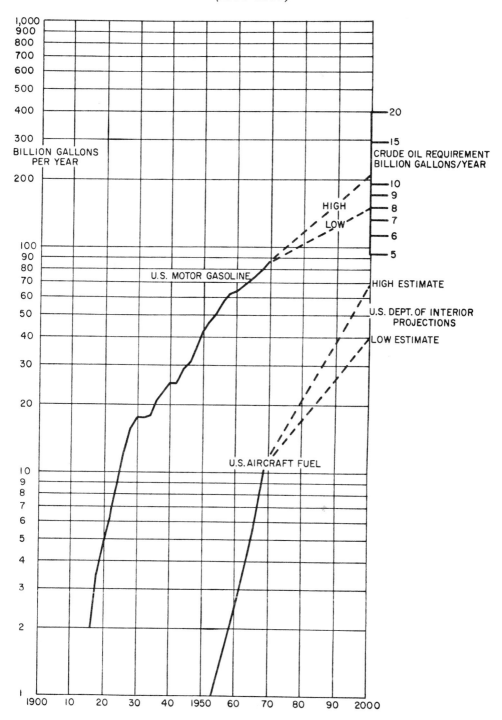

the United States produced 3.35 billion barrels from domestic sources in 1970 and imported 0.5 billion, for a total of 3.85 billion barrels of crude. As a rule of thumb, we can say that it takes slightly more than two barrels of crude to turn out one barrel of gasoline. This means that in terms of resource requirements, a 5-billion-barrel annual gasoline demand means more than 10 billion barrels of crude-oil demand.

The U.S. Department of the Interior has made a high and a low year-2000 projection of gasoline demand as shown on the chart. The crude oil required to supply the "high" corresponds to 11 billion barrels for the year 2000. Similar estimates for the future demand by jet aircraft for naphtha-kerosene-type fuels show that by the year 2000 the U.S. consumption of air-craft fuels could equal all gasoline consumption in 1964. However, we cannot apply the right-hand scale in Figure 7-4 to the jet-fuel curve for the simple reason that when a barrel of crude is processed to produce gasoline, the refinery, in its first "cut," produces jet fuel. The crude-oil scale in the illustration is subject to technological revision, since it is possible to design refineries in which as much as 70 percent of the input is converted into gasoline. This is technically possible with the new hydrocatalytic refineries in which hydrogen is added to distillates at high temperature and pressure. These hydro-crackers, as they are called, are not common today, and they are expensive.

The gasoline engine, which so revolutionized the American way of life and so fixed itself into the nation's economy, looms as the greatest fuel challenge of the future. It may be mandatory to shift from individual modes of travel to reliance on mass transit, and that will involve an energy switch that could increase the nation's demand for electric power. It adds one more complication to the already intricate problem of discerning the character of the energy picture in the future. Growth of energy supply in the United States has been stressed because of its fundamental importance to the economy and to the American life-style.

We could reexamine each of the various curves presented

in the preceding chapters to diagnose the limiting factors involved in their curvature, but many of these are already obvious. The cigarette curve, after hitting a plateau in the sixties following a century-long climb, is on the increase. This is presumably due to the zeal of tobacco companies in attempting to create new markets among the young and to allay fears of smokers with clever advertising campaigns. The warning *The Surgeon General Has Determined That Cigarette Smoking Is Dangerous to Your Health,* coupled with the federal order taking cigarette advertising off the TV screen and the radio, was a challenge to Madison Avenue. Having lost over a quarter billion dollars in advertising, the media manipulators switched their message to newspapers, magazines, and billboards. I recall one issue of the *Ladies' Home Journal* that contained about a dozen full-page cigarette ads. Result: the slump in tobacco sales was conquered, and a third of the U.S. population now smokes an average of four hundred packs a year—over a pack a day for the American smoker. Clearly, this is a case of the federal government versus the individual; the facts are well-known and have been widely publicized. The federal authorities are faced with what is essentially a political problem—overcoming the entrenched interests of tobacco-producing states as reflected in their congressional delegations.

Figure 7-5 is a display of the rapid growth of a truly American business, one closely linked to the marketing of mass production. This advertising business, the great persuader of the American scene, was exploited by the tobacco business from the start, especially on a national basis. Designed to create in the consumer a desire to buy something that he may or may not need or even want, advertising follows the mystique that product sales depend on the size of the advertising account. One would be remiss in discussing growth without including the growth curve of the U.S. advertising business. Now if it is true that Madison Avenue techniques can sell almost anything, one wonders if they could be used with reverse English—not to sell something.

This is being tried on national television spots by the American Cancer Society to fight lung cancer by citing the harmful effects of smoking. The results are in doubt because of the tobacco industry's quick switch to other media, once their ads were banned on TV.

It does seem incongruous for utilities to promote the use of natural gas and electricity through advertising, which they do at great expense. There is now pressure on the utilities to stop selling the kilowatt and, indeed, as an example of negative advertising, Consolidated Edison of New York even undertook a Save-a-Watt campaign to curb excessive use of electric energy.

FIGURE 7-5

U.S. ADVERTISING EXPENDITURES

The affluence of the U.S. advertising merchants is largely a postwar phenomenon, although it survived the Depression years by topping $1 billion annually. Newspapers claim about 30 percent of the market, and four-fifths of this is local advertising. Television, virtually nonexistent in the early 1950s, takes 20 percent of the revenues.

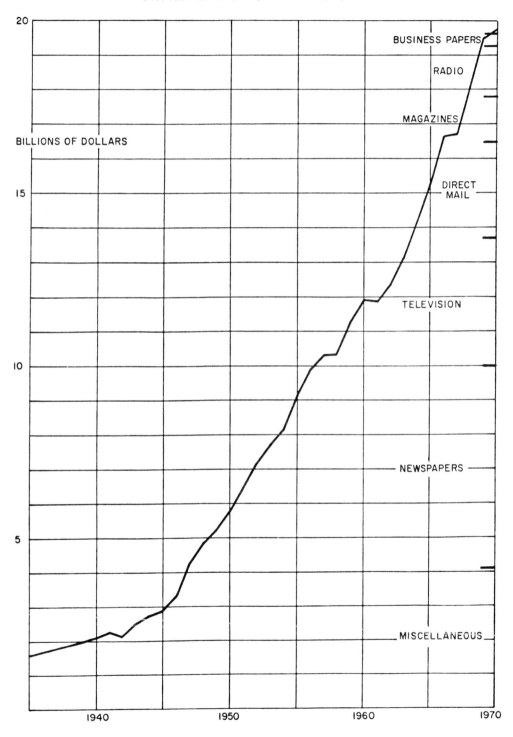

FIGURE 7-5

U.S. ADVERTISING EXPENDITURES

To return to the central question—Is all this growth necessary?—there is no single answer. One must pay a price for dropping down on the semilogarithmic curve to more modest increases or even to a plateau. In some cases, growth is so built in to our way of life, for example, the automobile, that to slow growth is to invite severe economic repercussions. And we are not yet living in a truly technological era, one in which everything is governed by computer programs and think-tank optimum analyses, with print-out instructions on the "best" way for society to proceed. Until that ill-starred time arrives, any cutbacks in growth must be subject to the give-and-take of democratic procedures and the rough-and-tumble of politics. The computer would tell us that it would be the "best" national policy to ban the sale of tobacco, for example, but that is not now politically feasible. Decisions to curtail growth must take political realities into account, not to mention personal choice, which, of course, includes the freedom to injure oneself.

In a democracy, the decision to curb growth must depend upon the tradition of the town hall—upon an openly debated resolution on which information is freely available. Here we come to the perplexing point that I have called the "torment of technology"—namely, the difficulty of subjecting technical issues to the public forum. Few will doubt that control of technology has become imperative in an age of exploitation. But how does a democracy construct the proper apparatus of control?

Because the consumption of fuels is rapidly moving in the direction of generating more electricity as the preferred form of energy, reaching 50 percent by the end of the century, the decision to curb energy growth becomes a matter of curtailing the kilowatt. And since the end use of electric energy is usually not more than a release of thermal energy, the problem of growth centers on resource adequacy to produce electric power and controls to protect the environment. Since electric-energy generation is increasingly of nuclear origin and will certainly dominate all energy sources in the next century, the question of growth in the long run focuses on nuclear-power stations. Given the success of the power-breeder and assuming that environmentalists maintain their vigilance regarding the licensing of nuclear stations, it would appear that technology would be capable of meeting the challenge of growth in the electric-energy sector. However, this assumes that the United States will control its population in the next century and that the growth curve for electric energy consumption will in fact bend over as consumer users saturate their demands.

CHAPTER

8

THE CONTROL OF TECHNOLOGY

If a society is to manage the growth of anything potentially injurious to itself, it must understand the nature of the threat. Adequate information is a precondition for prudent control. The benefits of technological innovations are usually more apparent than the adverse effects. Until the recent creation of the Environmental Protection Agency, the United States had no single governmental body specifically charged with responsibility for assessing the harmful effects of technology. Even now it is not at all clear how the federal government will weigh EPA evidence about potential environmental damage against the more obvious advantages of technological innovation.

Looking back over the record of the first two-thirds of the century, an orbital observer might indeed deduce that the free-enterprise system in the United States had functioned with virtually no controls. Industrialists and townspeople alike recognized that the factory smokestacks laid down a cruel and tissue-insulting chemical barrage on the adjacent population, but the workman was admonished to respect the belching stack as a sign of economic prosperity. The free-enterprise system was free to pollute. Coal-mine operators were free to condemn miners to underground deathtraps; as recently as 1947 more than 1,000 coal-mine fatalities occurred in a single year. In the first three decades of this century, the death toll in coal mines averaged more than 2,300 annually. Up to the present, more than 101,000 coal miners have lost their lives in cave-ins, flooding, mine fires, and other accidents. Despite the existing federal regulations governing mine safety, and a switch to strip and auger mining, 260 miners were killed in 1970.

One would have thought that such a technologically sophisticated agency as the Atomic Energy Commission would have been as meticulous in protecting the health of uranium miners as it was in safeguarding the radiation exposure of its laboratory personnel. Unfortunately, the AEC decided that uranium miners were not its responsibility, and the lamentable plight of overirradiated miners did not come to light until the 1960s. The life-shortening effect of long exposure to uraniferous mines is one of the oldest known industrial hazards, tracing back to lung disease noted in miners as early as 1500. The Joachimsthal mines of Erz Gebirge, Bohemia, worked for their precious metal content, but now known to contain radioactive minerals, caused miners to die in their prime. Radioactivity was not discovered until 1895, but an 1878 investigation of the miners' illness disclosed that they had lung cancer.

Automobile manufacturers, who could spend billions of dollars to bend metal into more grotesque forms each year, found it inconvenient to investigate the pollutant emissions from internal-combustion engines. Result: they had to be dragged kicking and screaming into meeting the 1975 automotive-emission standards. Their total effort has been directed toward turning out higher-horsepower cars, as Figure 8-1 partially illustrates. Fortunately, automotive engineers managed to achieve high horsepower by going to high-compression engines, which utilize high-octane fuel with comparative efficiency, otherwise gasoline consumption would have soared. Even then, over the past thirty years the national average use of motor fuel has dropped from 14 to 12 miles per gallon.

196

Tetraethyl lead is the gasoline additive that made use of the high-compression engine possible; ordinary refinery runs of gasoline are too low in octane to accommodate the horsepower. Adding a small amount of lead brings regular gas to 94-octane, and adding more to premium gas produces 100-octane fuel. (Originally General Motors and Standard Oil of New Jersey owned the Ethyl Corporation.) Putting lead into gas soon became big business, and during the sixties alone a total of 4,170 million pounds of lead were used in gasoline. In 1970 the Ethyl Corporation chalked up $205 million in sales of its leaded-gas compound. Through the expedient of adding lead to motor fuel, Detroit managed to market 300-hp cars that had a rather high level of fuel efficiency. It took no special perspicacity to foresee that very large quantities of lead, long notorious for its toxicity, would soon be exhausted into the air, but neither General Motors nor the Ethyl Corporation undertook any research on the long-term biological hazards. Nor did the U.S. government intervene until very recently. The removal of all lead from motor fuel, a process that will take much of the next decade to complete, is important for new cars; lead poisons the catalysts now used for automotive-emission control.

Once consumer habits are established, it is hard to change them. Drivers have been accustomed to the brand names of leaded gasolines and are slow to switch to new products, even if their cars can use unleaded gas. Late in 1971, the largest distributor of Texaco gas in the Washington, D.C. area told me that only about one customer in a hundred asked for unleaded gas. For one thing, the cost was higher than for leaded gas of comparable octane rating. When people are told that a familiar product is potentially harmful, they are likely to be skeptical. The average person has no direct evidence of lead toxicity and must therefore put his faith in some authority. When that authority has allowed a product to be freely marketed for four decades, the average person may wonder about the urgency of the ban against it.

More and more, the public is asked to trust an authority

more or less blindly. It is becoming increasingly difficult for the public to understand technology, and it is mystified when, as in the case of pesticides, products are allowed to be marketed in large volumes and are then indicted as detrimental to health. For over two decades scientists have occupied high advisory posts in government and have themselves been prominent in the public eye. At all levels of government, agencies have sprouted scientific-advisory committees and consultative bodies, ranging from the working level in the field right on up to the White House.

FIGURE 8-1

AVERAGE U.S. AUTO HORSEPOWER

Over the past half-century the power under the hood of the average American automobile has increased sixfold. The curve shows the average horsepower of all U.S. prime movers and not the maximum marketed by Detroit; nonetheless, it reflects the trend as American motorists have rocketed ahead from the 60-octane gas of the Depression to the 100-octane superpowered road monsters of the sixties. The twenty-year escalation of power under the Cadillac's bonnet ranges from a modest 160 hp in its 1951 model to 400 hp in its 390-cubic-inch displacement engine. Today the average higher-priced car packs at least ten times the power of comparable 1920 models.

FIGURE 8-1

AVERAGE U.S. AUTO HORSEPOWER

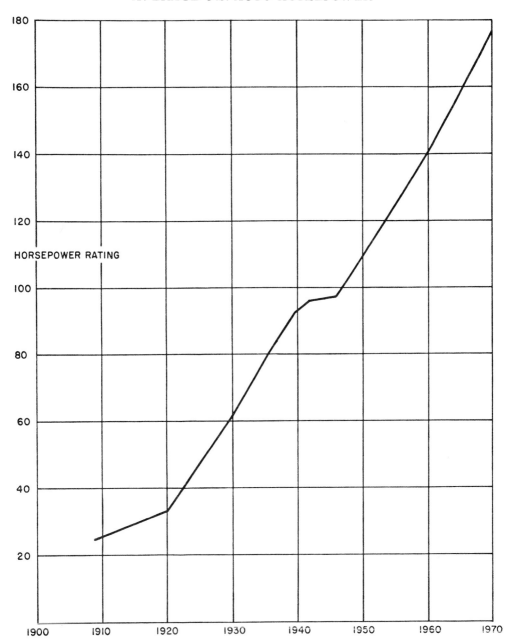

At top levels in government, scientists advise through a number of channels. The president has his science adviser and also the President's Science Advisory Committee (PSAC), which is composed of eminent scientists. Then there is the Office of Science and Technology and the Federal Council for Science and Technology. Both are in the Executive Office Building next to the White House, and across the street is the National Science Foundation, with a thousand people on its staff. Farther up Pennsylvania Avenue is the National Academy of Sciences, which was created by the Congress over a century ago and which carries out studies on a wide variety of scientific and technical topics. Then there is the Environmental Protection Agency and the Federal Food and Drug Administration, as well as the Department of Agriculture. The federal agencies have in all a total of about two thousand advisory bodies. It is no exaggeration to state that the White House has funneled to it the collective advice of thousands of highly qualified scientists. Nor is it in question that the quality of this scientific counsel is of high caliber. But there is a cruel paradox which Professor Martin L. Perl, in a 1971 article in *Science,* phrased as follows:

> How have we gotten into so much technological trouble while getting so much well-intentioned and correct technological advice?

Dr. Perl illustrates the paradox by pointing out that in the spring of 1963 the President's Science Advisory Committee issued a report, *Use of Pesticides.* The report recommends a cutback in the use of persistent pesticides, beginning with government restrictions on "wide-scale use of such persistent pesticides (such as DDT) except for the necessary control of disease vectors." Yet the government allowed the mass production of DDT and other equally toxic insecticides, and it did not begin following the PSAC advice until 1971—and then only after the issue had been dramatized in the press and public pressure to effect reforms had mounted.

Having lived in metropolitan Washington for a quarter of

a century, during which time I have followed the buildup of a top-heavy science advisory superstructure, I find it all too easy to pinpoint the reason for Dr. Perl's paradox. To be given advice is one thing—to take it is quite another. Furthermore, it is all too common for a scientific advisory group to deliberate and make recommendations on an issue, then submit a report and forget about it. In fact, I once attended a scientific meeting at which Edward David, President Nixon's science adviser, argued that scientists should be analysts and not advocates. I think that Dr. David's advice bisects a scientist-citizen into two noncommunicating bodies; it tells the scientist to analyze a problem and list choices or options, but not to advocate *any*.

Also dampening to the spirit of advocacy in scientific-advisory circles is the screening process that goes on before a "new man" is permitted to join the advisory elite. A committee tends to be a self-replicating device, creating new membership in its own image. The in-group elects to admit only new members who give promise, from past performance, of being committee-broken. If scientist-advisers find that well-founded and precisely targeted advice is not heeded, they may grouse among themselves and even make brave noises in committee, but rarely do their grievances erupt into public dissension. To paraphrase the Bible—the meek shall inherit the advisory posts of government.

In the past, advisory committees met in a cozy atmosphere either of official secrecy or, at least, without any public observers being present. The Freedom of Information Act of 1967 served as a wedge in the door of federal committee rooms, and in 1972 Executive Order 11671 stipulated that meetings of federal advisory bodies would be open to the public. The impact of this ruling has yet to be sensed, but clearly another path was opened to permit those outside the federal establishment to gain a foothold in the critical area of advice giving. The significance of this elevated perch in the federal hierarchy is that it allows access to information early enough to permit intervention on a timely scale. Too often the public is confronted with edicts about programs or projects and must scurry around to piece together a reasonable opposition position.

Perhaps the real paradox here is that the scientists are the true revolutionaries of this century; they have literally convulsed it. But the community of science lacks the political clout common to many smaller groups. The modern miracle men, so gigantic in the laboratory, are political pygmies.

Yet in the closing third of the century we confront problems that are unique in history. Entire species of flora and fauna, established through the millennia, may be threatened by some new technological innovation. Men are called upon to bury in perpetuity certain radioactive wastes—yet there are nations, such as Belgium and Japan, to name but two, that have no acceptable nuclear graveyard sites. The above-surface traffic in radioactive wastes strains previously tolerable standards of transportation safety.

So far as nuclear hazards are concerned, the Atomic Energy Commission, which I regard as the most technologically proficient of federal agencies, has very low public credibility. Its decision to recommend siting a Radioactive Waste Repository at Lyons, Kansas (now rejected), elicited strong objections from Governor Robert Docking. In mid-1971 he wrote to the AEC:

> The final statement as prepared by the Atomic Energy Commission offers no scientific proof of the safety of the proposed Lyons project. It offers only pledges to have faith in the AEC. Our experiences with officials of the AEC in the past few months have given us ample reasons not to have faith in the AEC.

If the people or their elected representatives do not have faith in the AEC in a field where the agency's technical prowess is superior to any other's, whom are they to trust? The issue is raised at hearings of Atomic Safety and Licensing Boards when intervenors challenge the safety of a nuclear-power plant or its environmental impact. The old question,

How safe is safe?, has new meaning when applied to siting a nuclear-power unit near a metropolitan population.

In connection with the issue of nuclear safety, I recall that I spoke on the subject "How safe is safe enough—and why?" on November 15, 1972, before the conference of the American Nuclear Society. It seemed rather an *ex post facto* discussion of nuclear issues, but I advanced the following argument. Assume, I said, that a nuclear accident took place near a city and that there was a loss of life and extensive property damage. How soon would the community allow a new nuclear plant to be built nearby? I stated that ten years was obviously too soon and a thousand years was too long; a hundred years seemed a reasonable estimate. Then, estimating the total number of reactors to be deployed in a century, I deduced that a nuclear plant would have to be built so as to have less than one chance in a million of such an accident occurring in one year. Unfortunately, the state of the nuclear art is such that it is not possible to make substantive predictions of reactor safety in such a low range of probability. Alas, the fact that the U.S. nuclear industry has accumulated a relatively small number of years with a score of operating reactors provides little basis for confidence, since the statistical base is too limited to apply to a low probability event.

Technology is now on trial. Many people have already concluded that scientists have committed many sins against society. The works of science, as applied through technology, loom so large in the public mind that people make the false assumption that scientists are in control. When something associated with technological innovation goes wrong, the public indicts science.

Even if scientists *were* in charge, the fact remains that we have entered a world of bewildering complexity and change. A pharmaceutical firm that develops a new drug is understandably eager to market it to make up for its research and development expenses, and the public is all too ready to buy. This combination of circumstances does not make for a happy ambience in which to investigate the possible adverse or long-term detrimental effects of the drug. The public is all too prone to equate science with certainty and to believe that the experimental method of analysis is capable of unlimited precision. Unfortunately, animal studies are limited both in the magnitude of a population that can be investigated experimentally and in their applicability to human beings. There will always be *some* risk associated with the widespread use of a drug.

The U.S. public has been conditioned to expect miracles from science. To the GIs in the Pacific, waiting to invade Japan, the A-bomb was a miracle. To the mother with a seriously ill child, penicillin was a miracle. DDT, as used to eliminate malaria, *was* a chemical miracle. But in the aftermath of miracles come doubts, disillusion, and despair. The A-bomb led to the H-bomb, to an immensely expensive missile race, and to "peace through mutual terror." Many miracle drugs have turned out to have disastrous side effects. And DDT has ricocheted through the environment interrupting the reproductive cycles of fish-eating birds through eggshell thinning. Science, which had been elevated to an altitude of great eminence, has undergone a deflation as an antiscience movement gathered strength. As Derek J. de Solla Price observed in 1971, the reaction to science may be "an 'anti-science' movement in which science is viewed as useless, irrelevant to the needs of society, or even actively destructive of humanistic objectives. It may take the form of a regression to mysticism and to intuition, to subjective and ad-hoc judgment, and the avoidance of the sciences whose growth has made them less and less attainable and comprehensible to the non-expert bulk of the population."

In the fall of 1971 the federal government made a U-turn on its phosphate policy for detergents. Having condemned the use of household detergents as contributing to the eutrophication of waterways and lakes (i.e., excessive biological growth manifest as algal blooms), federal authorities reversed themselves and decided that phosphates were not so bad after all. The public tends to become exasperated with such administrative flip-flops and to place less and less confidence in federal authority.

Then there is the case of DDT-like chemical compounds called polychlorinated biphenyls (PCBs), manufactured by Monsanto Chemical Company. PCBs are compounds with high chlorine content that can withstand quite high temperatures, such as those occurring in ordinary incinerators. They are used for a variety of industrial purposes—as plasticizers, in carbonless duplicating paper, in heat-exchange fluids, and as additives to inks, plastics, and insecticides. PCB is not soluble in water but does enter readily into oils and fats. "PCB is now universally distributed in the terrestrial, freshwater and marine environment of North America," testified Dr. Robert Risebrough before the U.S. Senate Commerce Committee in August 1971. The scientist on the staff of the Bodega Marine Laboratory of the University of California found measurable amounts of PCB in remote lakes in the Arctic terrain of northern Quebec. Body fat of the peregrine falcon (California) was found to contain two thousand parts per million of PCB.

How did PCB wend its way through the various pathways of the environment? No one is quite sure. Some has undoubtedly entered the atmosphere by surviving combustion in incinerators. Unlike DDT, it was not deliberately introduced into the environment, and this, along with the difficulty of measuring it in small quantities, may explain why the PCB hazard did not attract as much attention as DDT and other toxic insecticides. The Federal Food and Drug Administration learned about PCB contamination in June 1971 when the FDA's Total Diet Market Basket showed PCB residues in cereals such as shredded wheat. The PCB was traced to the paperboard used for packaging the foods.

The American public scarcely enjoys technological surprises in its food packages, and the PCB story can only serve to make citizens more skeptical of federal competence in the protection of public health. Inevitably, though he is not responsible, the scientist's stature shrinks with each new disclosure, and the public gravitates toward a know-nothing attitude.

Adverse effects of technology do not stop at national borders. It is quite possible for pollutant effluents, for example, to drift from the Ruhr and affect the environment in Sweden. We have already mentioned the global implications of increasing the carbon dioxide content of the atmosphere through combustion of greater quantities of fossil fuel. But even more precipitous climatic changes might be induced by certain arctic alterations, such as coating the snow-ice surface with a heat-absorbing dust. In short, the planet is no longer large, compared with the impact of technological innovation; the possibility of irreversible changes in the world environment must be acknowledged.

The control of technology now ranks as an urgent national and international necessity. As we shall observe in the next chapter, other nations are on a lower, but sharply ascendant, part of their growth curves, and we must accept that worldwide consumption of electric energy, for example, will impose very heavy demands on the total supply of all fuels. And unless stringent controls are applied on effluents of all kinds, the global pollution hazard will mount. The more technologically mature nations must take the lead in devising and implementing a system of controls that brings the most toxic effluents down to tolerable levels. Unless they set a good example, the world will wallow in a festering trough as developing nations follow the leaders.

If the planet's biosphere is to be maintained at a standard compatible with a high quality of life, we must know how various additives to the environment are ending up in the air, water, and soil (their "fate"), and we must be able to trace their sources. This means that a planetary system of monitoring must be undertaken as a global warning-and-control network. We need to know when new effluents crop up, and we must maintain a constant surveillance over the concentrations of any such material in the environmental pathways. Our knowledge of the source, distribution, concentration mechanisms, and ultimate fate of many toxic materials is totally inadequate. Intensified research is required to provide the information.

The world's attention was focused on the global dispersion of a spectacular pollutant in the spring of 1954 when the United States tested a very powerful nuclear weapon at Bikini Atoll. The local fallout of radioactive material from the bomb cloud aroused the world because of the direct effect of debris on some two hundred Marshall Islanders and twenty-three Japanese fishermen. The fishermen happened to be some ninety-two miles from the Bikini explosion when their tiny boat was caught in heavy fallout that produced direct biological effects on the men, including epilation (loss of hair), skin burns, and signs of radiation sickness. The islanders were removed from the contaminated atolls and given prompt medical aid; they appeared to recover with few lingering effects. Some two decades later, however, the children who had been irradiated developed abnormalities of the thyroid and had to undergo surgery. Both the immediate and the delayed effects were clearly associated with the large doses of radiation inflicted on people over a short period of time.

Global concern over radioactive fallout centered on the debris swept up in the bomb cloud and transported to high altitudes where the winds aloft dispersed it to the four corners of the earth. Nonetheless, scientists were able to measure the gradual descent of radioactive particles as they were borne to earth by all forms of precipitation. This radioactive drizzle persisted for years and led to gradual accumulations of certain long-lived species of atoms, such as cesium 137 and strontium 90. The U.S. Atomic Energy Commission launched a worldwide system of monitoring the fallout and measured its concentration in plants, animals, milk, and cereals and even in human bone. As a result of the injection of a few hundred pounds of long-lived radioactive elements into the stratosphere, every living person born on the planet, not just the Lapps mentioned in Chapter 5, bears in his bones measurable quantities of radioactivity. Here was a case where a single act of technology set off a chain of events almost beyond comprehension. The amount of that radioactivity is only a small fraction of the radiation dose delivered by the natural environment, but it *is* measurable.

How dangerous is the low level of radioactivity produced by weapons testing? The question is unresolved. Many years of intensive research have not provided a solid answer. The amount of radiation is so small that animal experiments with mice, beagles, or fruit flies do not yield positive results, only a range of estimates of possible effects. Suppose, for example, a scientist carries out an experiment involving the irradiation of one thousand beagles and finds no statistically valid biological effect that he can assign to the radiation. He cannot exclude the possibility that if he had used ten thousand beagles he might have found an effect, or that if he had used ten times more radiation there would still *not* have been an effect. The point is that pushing the validity of the data to apply to a total population of 3.5 billion people takes the scientist beyond the limits of his experiment or of any experiment he can reasonably hope to get funding for.

The inability of science to determine the biological effects of low-level fallout had direct bearing on the great public concern over nuclear-power effluent hazards in 1969–71. But in regard to radiation hazards, the scientific community did have records dating back to 1895 on the biological effects of X rays and radium. As a result, maximum permissible limits had been set for occupational exposure to radiation. With larger numbers of people potentially at risk from radiation at the beginning of the postwar growth of atomic energy, these limits were revised downward. Soon scientists were called upon to suggest new limits that would safeguard the very young, the sick, and those with unusual sensitivity to radiation. Unlike workers occupationally exposed, the general population would not be under control either administratively, with respect to exposure, or medically, for surveillance and treatment. Therefore, "permissible" levels for the general population were arbitrarily set tenfold lower than for smaller occupational groups.

The Atomic Energy Commission came under severe criticism for the radiation standards it set for effluent releases from nuclear-power plants, even though it had complied with the recommendations of such standard-setting groups as the Federal Radiation Council, which was then authorized to make the recommendations. Although the actual operation of nuclear-power plants produced radiation doses to nearby population far lower than the national standards permitted, the AEC did not reduce its radiation limits until June 1971. At that time it made drastic reductions in the allowable effluent releases and made it very difficult for its critics to quarrel with the standards.

Complete freedom from risk cannot be guaranteed by any radiation standards susceptible to measurement by monitoring instruments. The public will always have to accept some degree of risk, whether from proximity to a nuclear-power plant, or from pesticides in the environment, or from industrial pollutants in the biosphere.

The control of environmental pollutants becomes a vexing problem when, as in the case of sulfur oxide emission, it becomes necessary to impose restrictions on fuels. If an East Coast utility is prohibited from burning high-sulfur coal and cannot gain access to low-sulfur coal, as is not unusual, then it is forced to use an alternative fuel, such as residual oil or natural gas. Gas will probably not be an available option because of Federal Power Commission control of its allocations, and the utility may have trouble getting enough low-sulfur residual oil. Under such conditions a community might be forced to make a cruel choice between sulfurous pollution and reduced electric energy.

Large as these control problems may appear to be, they are dwarfed by the much more complex issue of resource control. In attacking that problem, a modern industrial society must be capable of planning over a twenty-, thirty-, and

209

fifty-year time base. Such long-term projection of national needs is new to the American experience, and it conflicts with the much shorter-term time focus of elected political leaders whose eyes are fixed on two, four, and six years ahead when they run for office.

If a nation is going to go the route of high technology, that is, pursue a Ph.D.-based economy, then it must also reform its political guidance. Back in 1965 I wrote a book titled *The New Priesthood,* referring to the Ph.D. elite of our society, and urged that a Department of Science consider the societal impact of projects and programs prior to their being launched. "Such planning," I wrote, "could act as a sort of early warning system to appraise well in advance the potential repercussions of modern scientific developments." No such department came into being, although the Congress did finally establish, some eight years later, an Office of Technological Assessment as a kind of over-the-horizon mechanism for anticipating the adverse effects of technological venture. To my mind, the Section 102 clause of the National Environmental Policy Act, which went into effect in 1971, became a vehicle for technological assessment, although it was limited to environmental impact.

President Nixon's June 1971 energy message to the Congress must be viewed as an "opener"—as a preface to crisis, warning in a noncrisis manner of the nation's necessity to conserve fuel in the future. But oil, the most critical natural resource in the U.S. energy future, was dealt with in a circuitous manner. The president skirted the critical problem of oil imports, holding out hope that America's vast resources in the form of coal and oil shale would become a bountiful source of synthetic oil. Most important, the White House message made no quantitative assessment of future demand and supply—no year-2000 estimates, for example—of what it would take to keep America mobile. The real energy crisis for the U.S. future centers on the gasoline supply. The United States must manage to lay rational plans for meeting its automotive needs in 1990 and 2000 as well, and it must adopt a policy that will provide a means of avoiding disruptive imbalance in transportation systems should fuel supplies run short. This is a peculiarly difficult challenge for a democracy in that while it can project gasoline needs into the future, a reverse planning of making the demand fit the supply presents many problems. Their resolution would require a high degree of coordination and control by a number of federal agencies. The federal government has to make a major decision at the outset—either to adjust demand to the probable supply or to accept a demand figure and attempt to meet it with a concerted effort to increase the supply, such as an accelerated program of oil synthesis or increased oil imports. However, the critical decision will be strongly affected by influential oil interests, which have never been stingy when it comes to financing political campaigns.

Assuming that the weight of available evidence tips the balance of decision in favor of tempering demand to the dictates of supply, how might this then be implemented in terms of fuel policy on gasoline? There are many levers that might be used to alter the mechanism of fuel consumption, but it will take a sense of urgency, a note of crisis, plus rare political fortitude, to shift gears downward on demand. A sense of crisis is hard to communicate a decade or two in advance—and this is precisely what impends in the case of gasoline. Most Americans, even if distrustful of technology because of its errant ways, have a deep-down feeling that it can solve any problems, provided it is given enough money. This is, in a sense, a manifestation of the frontier spirit—of unbounded faith in the much-vaunted American know-how. But we have seen how even the Mesabi Range was exhausted and how U.S. oil fields are being depleted by the gaping maw of the industrial machine. The United States is what scientists call "a bounded system," that is, one with finite boundaries. It has only so much area and so much water, and its underground resources are finite. No longer can it annex new territory, and it must therefore live within its own resource limitations by exploiting new technology, or moderate its demands, or look abroad for the means of satisfying its material needs.

Happily, as the United States depletes its natural resources so long stored beneath the ground, it has the option of exercising a new resource whose center of gravity is about five feet above ground level. This is the accumulated brainpower of a technologically advanced society. It is a waste of time to hunt witches and seek to pillory scientists and technologists as responsible for national ills; they have never been in the driver's seat. If technology is to be controlled, if it is to be used wisely, and if its ill effects are to be avoided, the nation needs not castigation but leadership that combines the technical skills of specialists with the responsible management of those charged with our political administration.

CHAPTER

9

THE AFFLUENT ISLAND

Malthus wrote his prophetic essay warning of overpopulation of the planet as the American colonies were struggling to cling together, and at a time when the world's population was approaching the billion mark. It appeared hardly likely then that the United States, little more than a sprawling beachhead on a vast continent, would spearhead a revolution in world industrial affairs. Environmentalists are probably bemoaning the lack of an "industrial" Malthus to warn about the dangers of overproduction of goods—of runaway consumption—rather than of people.

To put the problem of world population in perspective, the historical record has been plotted in Figure 9-1. Since Stone Age people handed down no census records, we must infer population for those prehistoric days, but it is not unreasonable to set down a record such as has been done. If nothing else, it illustrates rather vividly the swift ascent of populations in this century—a rise that is closely linked to man's further exploits in industrialization.

Perhaps the most graphic way of depicting the growth of world population is to set down the dates for the billion-people points on a curve alongside the number of years it took to add the last billion (see Table 9-1).

TABLE 9-1

World Population	Date	Years to Add Last Billion
1 billion	1825	—
2 billion	1930	105
3 billion	1960	30
4 billion	1976	16
5 billion	1988	12
6 billion	1997	9

FIGURE 9-1

WORLD POPULATION (8000 B.C.–*2000* A.D.*)*

This graph of the growth of the world's population illustrates the difficulty of depicting extreme variations graphically. Because of the limited food supply before the beginning of agriculture, it is estimated that the world population never exceeded 10 million during the Stone Age. Showing that comparatively low figure and the world's present 6 billion on the same chart is a cumbersome process. This chart again demonstrates the "straight-line" fallacy. A medieval historian with such a chart in hand would have been justified in predicting a world population of no more than half a billion by the year 2000. Present demographers put the figure at 6–7 billion.

FIGURE 9-1

WORLD POPULATION (8000 B.C.–2000 A.D.)

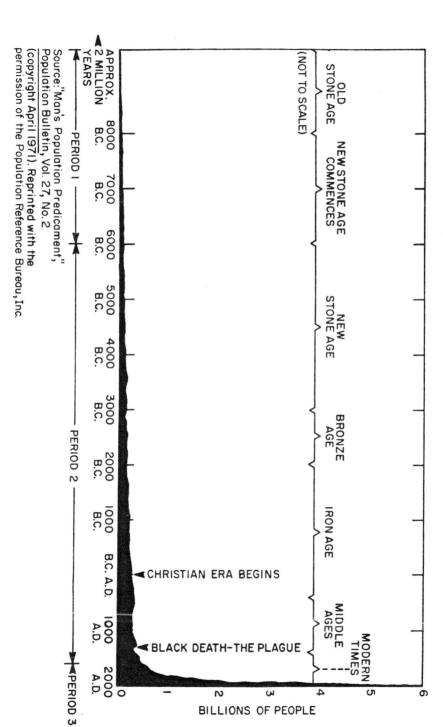

Source: "Man's Population Predicament,"
Population Bulletin, Vol. 27, No. 2
(copyright April 1971). Reprinted with the
permission of the Population Reference Bureau, Inc.

Our estimates up to the year 2000 are not likely to be far off the mark if we use a worldwide 2 percent annual increase in population, a figure accurately reflecting the present growth rates. At a growth rate of 1 percent per year, Figure 9-2 shows that the U.S. population will be somewhat under 300 million by the year 2000, about 4.5 percent of the world total. Projecting beyond the year 2000 is an "iffy" proposition. If we assume that the 2 percent growth rate will continue without letup, then the world census in 2100

FIGURE 9-2

U.S. AND WORLD POPULATION PROJECTIONS

On a population chart that begins with 100 million, the United States is not an entry until after the first decade of this century. Just before the Civil War, the U.S. population was only 2 percent of the world total. It had risen to about 6 percent a hundred years later. The present worldwide annual growth rate is about 2 percent. If that rate continued, the planet would have some 43 to 51 billion inhabitants by 2100, with 2 billion of them looking for breathing space in the United States. Population curves for the world and for the United States are also projected at lower rates (dotted lines).

FIGURE 9-2

U.S. AND WORLD POPULATION PROJECTIONS

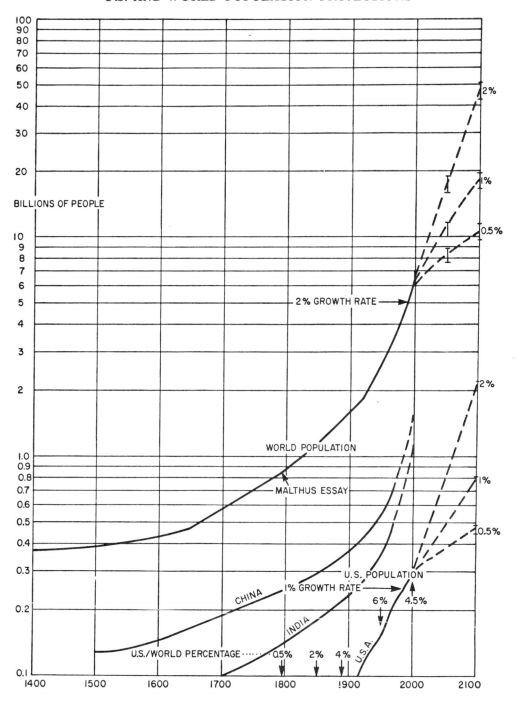

will comprise some 43 to 51 billion persons. If, however, population controls take effect and the curve is held at a 1 percent per year growth, then at the end of the next century the planet will have about 18 billion inhabitants. Cutting this growth rate in half—a monumental "if"—would bend the curve over, and the world population would be only somewhat in excess of 10 billion.

Extrapolating the U.S. population on a 2 percent per year basis, for the sake of comparison, gives a figure of 2 billion by the end of the twenty-first century. But continuation of the 1 percent rate projects half a billion U.S. inhabitants within a hundred years and only three-quarter billion by 2100. More realistically and hopefully, the U.S. population-growth curve will follow the course of the lowest projection in Figure 9-2 and will not reach the half billion level until sometime in the twenty-second century, and it may conceivably be programmed to keep below this "limit" for the indefinite future. In that case it would approach a stationary state and would continue to be less than 5 percent, perhaps as low as 1 percent, of the global population in 2100.

Rather than add to the torrent of words warning of overpopulation, let us look at the stresses created by our own "island affluence": How long can the United States, constituting only 5 percent of the world's population, continue to exploit such an inequitable proportion of its natural resources? Over the longer term, an evolving issue of even greater significance is the Malthusian-associated problem of world production of *things*. Will the nations close to the top rung of the industrial ladder aspire to U.S. affluence and emulate it by mass production of motorcars and other consumer items? At what rate will the less-developed nations struggle to climb up from the lower rungs of the ladder and follow the ascendancy of the United States and certain European nations?

When we venture into such projections we depart from the comfortable data base of the United States and invade a strange land with few signposts to mark the way into the future. Clearly, we are well advised to keep our projections this side of the year 2000 as we go beyond the territorial borders of the United States and attempt to assess the shape of the world's future. We may begin by selecting electric energy, a growth area where the various nations of the world agree upon a common unit of production and where the data base is substantial. Figure 9-3 shows the lower output of the industrially developed nations of the world, excepting Japan whose postwar recovery has made it a major factor in the world economy. A separate curve has been plotted for Japan, illustrating how the wartime bombing shattered its industrial vitality. But since this devastation, Japan has doubled its electric-energy output every six and one-half years, even though it is virtually fuel-less and dependent upon imports for over 90 percent of its energy production. With one-seventh the population of China, Japan uses more than four times as much electric energy. On a per capita basis, China has a vast energy gap, which will undoubtedly widen as Japan holds her population in check while China's booms.

Japan is sighting on a goal of 2,500-billion-kwh annual production in the year 2000, four-fifths of which will be supplied by nuclear power. The Pan-Asia curve, which includes Japan, is the riskiest of all projections, but it reflects the realities of power in that (a) it requires large amounts of capital to build large electric-power stations, (b) sheer construction is demanding, and the Japanese record in doubling its electric capacity in six and one-half years is phenomenal, and (c) consumption of large amounts of electric energy requires a corresponding high-demand economy to absorb it. For example, the Japanese electric consumption for the year 2000 amounts to about two-thirds of the planned U.S. figure of over 30,000 kwh per capita for that year. Our Asian estimate, subtracting the Japanese total, leaves only 2,500 billion kwh for the mainland and its estimated 3.5 billion population in the year 2000. On this basis, the average per capita electric-energy use on the Asian continent in the year 2000 would be about 700 kwh per year, the U.S. per capita consumption in the late 1920s—leaving an eighty-year affluence gap between the Asians and the Americans. Each American will be consuming more than forty times as much electric energy as the average Asian, and I suspect the discrepancy will be even greater.

Is this estimate too pessimistic? On the contrary, I think it allows for a very determined effort on the part of India and China, the twin giants of the great land mass, to produce electric power. It assumes that the Japanese will slow their rate of electric development, changing to a doubling time of

FIGURE 9-3

WORLD CONSUMPTION OF ELECTRIC ENERGY

The electric-energy curves for the world, for all of North America, for the United States, and for Europe have conformed rather closely since 1930 and are expected to continue to do so until about the last decade of the century, when U.S. consumption will begin to reach the saturation point. Russia's curve has climbed more steeply. By the year 2000, the annual electricity consumption of the industrially developed nations of the West and Russia will equal 31 trillion kwh. The separate curve for Japan shows the deep declivity caused by the wartime bombing. Since that devastation, Japan has doubled its electric-energy output every six and a half years. Projection of the world total (continued in the lower right-hand corner) is based on the sum of the continental totals, plus a token amount for Oceania. It climbs to 38 trillion kwh for the year 2000.

FIGURE 9-3

WORLD CONSUMPTION OF ELECTRIC ENERGY

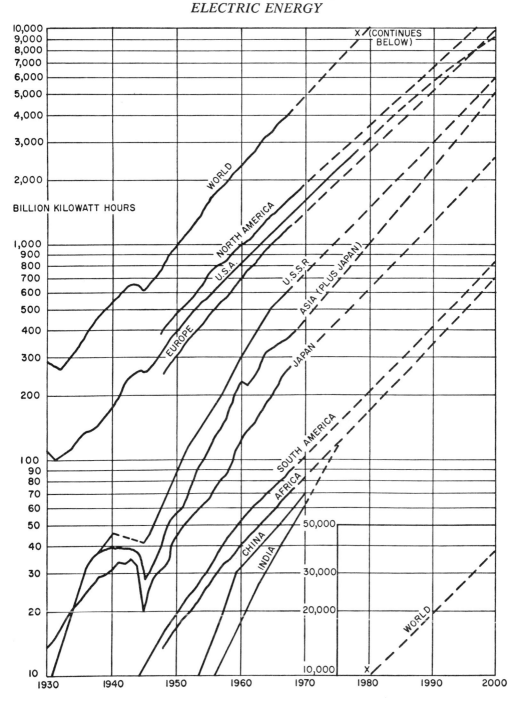

ten years. India must rely mainly upon nuclear power, since the subcontinent has very limited fossil-fuel resources. India has undertaken an ambitious nuclear program which, although I have no solid evidence on this score, I think is aimed at attaining the 1-trillion-kwh production rate before the end of the century. R. L. Datta, of the Central Salt and Marine Chemicals Research Institute, Bhavnagar, points out: "India accounts for 15 percent of the world population and only 1.5 percent of the energy consumption of the world." In a National Academy of Sciences report in 1972, the Indian energy expert noted that over half of India's energy came from burning dung, firewood, and vegetable waste and that kerosene was the "universal illuminant" of the country. India's determined effort to yank itself from its low-energy status is keyed to three energy sources—oil which it must import, hydropower which it has at hand, and nuclear power which is being exploited rather aggressively. But all these forms of energy require capital, and this may be for India, as for many other nations, the roadblock to nuclear-electric power. India has set its energy sights on achieving a 35-million-kilowatt electric capacity by 1975–76, which would imply an energy production of 120 billion kwh of electricity. If this installation of electric power can be achieved, then power growth in India will parallel that of Japan in the 1960s. But a nation with a per capita income of not much more than one hundred dollars per year will face a severe challenge in financing the thermal, hydro, and nuclear plants required to sustain such projected power growth. China's electric future is highly speculative but is probably somewhat more ambitious than India's. In both cases, the future seems too uncertain for extrapolation on the chart. The curve for Asia, as extrapolated in Figure 9-3, is a shaky projection encompassing the probable totals for Iran, Iraq, Singapore, Ceylon, Indonesia, Hong Kong, Thailand, Vietnam, and Pakistan. It is a dismal forecast; it assumes that well over half the world's population in the year 2000 will be consuming about 7 percent of its electric energy.

Including South America and Africa in this global-energy picture does not improve it. If one assumes that both continents will manage to double their electric capacity every twelve years, then together they will account for only about 4 percent of the world's electricity. A total of 38 trillion kwh of electric energy is estimated for the annual world consumption in the year 2000. This estimate is quite close to that made by Nobel Laureate Glenn T. Seaborg. Regarding the projections, Dr. Seaborg said: "The predictions for the year 2000 can be best described as presumptuous. The greatest population increases of all will be in the less-developed portions of the world. As more and more technologies shift from wood or camel-dung fires to electric-stoves, world electrical power will skyrocket."

If we assume that a figure of 38 trillion kwh as the world's annual consumption of electricity is not wide of the mark, what does this mean in terms of fuel use? We have already noted that two-thirds of the U.S. electric energy will be of nuclear origin, and about four-fifths of Japan's. India's electric future may also be predominantly nuclear, as will England's and much of Europe's. But much of the world's electric power, though probably less than half, will be supplied by fossil fuel. The world's fossil-fuel resources and the recent history of their exploitation as energy sources is therefore of direct interest.

A projection to the year 2000 (Fig. 9-4) calls for a doubling of the coal supply in the next thirty years. World coal reserves already determined by exploration amounts to perhaps 10 trillion tons, and the total estimated resources are about 17 trillion tons. There is, therefore, no doubt about the extent of coal reserves, but distribution and availability are another matter. The lion's share of the coal resources is found in Asia, especially in the U.S.S.R. and China, and in the United States. Africa and South America, on the other hand, are estimated to have a total of only 100 billion tons of coal in reserve. Getting coal out of the earth and transporting it pose problems that limit its utility in many areas. However, as the premium fuels run in short supply, increasing effort will be focused on converting coal to oil and gas, thus easing the transportation problem. The 5-billion-ton projection for the year 2000 assumes that large quantities of coal will be utilized in fuel synthesis.

Oil has played a relatively modest role in the world's fuel picture, but by mid-century it gave signs of becoming dominant globally, as it now is in the United States. Since oil is the premium fuel of the world, a separate chart has been drawn to show the world supply and the U.S. demand supply

FIGURE 9-4

WORLD CONSUMPTION OF ENERGY
(By Fuel Source)

The use of solid fuels for energy production (bottom line) has almost doubled since 1930. The projection to 2000 predicts that it will double again in thirty years. The chart uses the metric ton (2,204 pounds), the standard used in world-energy statistics, as the unit of measure. The projection of liquid fuels involves a year-2000 annual consumption of about 35 billion barrels. This is a somewhat more modest level than the present trend toward oil would indicate. It is, however, used as the basis for a conservative estimate of the world oil consumption in this chapter.

FIGURE 9-4

WORLD CONSUMPTION OF ENERGY
(by Fuel Source)

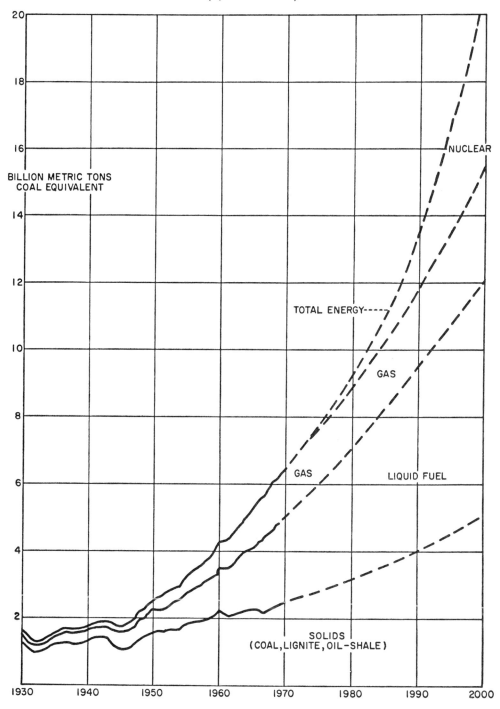

(Fig. 9-5). In the last decade or so of the century, the United States will probably enter the era of synthetic oil. This, if it proves economical and compatible with environmental security, will push up the U.S. production curve, which will nonetheless undoubtedly fall far short of demand.

Before World War II, the United States consumed two-thirds of all oil used in the world, but by 1960 the rest of the world was using as much oil as we were. Ten years later the other nations were consuming twice as much as the

FIGURE 9-5

WORLD OIL SUPPLY AND U.S. DEMAND

The U.S. demand for oil is extrapolated to the year 2000, when it is expected that up to 15 billion barrels will be used. The U.S. production of oil (bottom curve) is expected to peak in 1975, as old fields are pumped out and are not replaced by new ones. The top curve (world supply) has not been much affected by the decline in the U.S. production curve. The United States consumed half the world production in 1960, but only a third of it in 1970. The world projection is conservative. Failure of nuclear power to fulfill its goals and a willingness to overproduce from the Persian Gulf fields could shoot annual production to 50 billion barrels in the year 2000.

FIGURE 9-5

WORLD OIL SUPPLY AND U.S. DEMAND

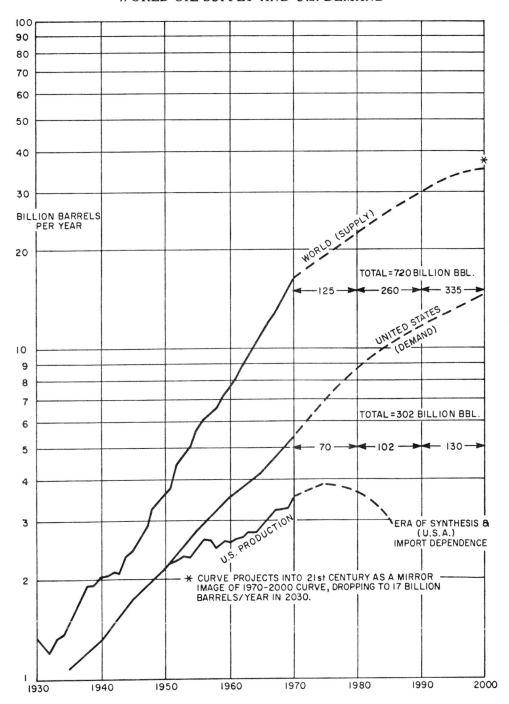

United States. Projecting the future oil supply for the world is not just a matter of lining up the points on a chart, though they do form a remarkably straight line for a quarter-century, and then projecting this indefinitely into the future. This would result in the phenomenal figure of 100 billion barrels of oil by the year 1993 rather than the more likely estimate of one-third that figure. Conservation of the world's reserves requires that some limits be imposed on pumping oil from the earth. We need to realize that the oil reserves are finite. A generous estimate of the ultimately recoverable oil in the world is about 2,000 billion barrels. If this is exploited conservatively, it will fit the estimated production of 35 billion barrels per year at the end of the century (Fig. 9-5).

This projection of the world oil supply represents a distinct change in the historic pattern of the oil industry. Rather than doubling every decade, the production would double only after two decades, flatten off, and then start downward. But the world's demand for oil will not end with the year 2000 and should in fact be on the increase, since oil is extremely versatile and well adapted to small-scale power production—especially for transportation purposes. It is not easy to extrapolate the world's consumption of energy from Figure 9-4, but if we plot the same data on a semi-log chart (Fig. 9-6), then a projection is easier. The growth rate for total energy has been relatively slow, and extending the same rate into the twenty-first century is not unreasonable. When this is done, the world's total energy consumption in the year 2070 turns out to be the equivalent of 110 billion metric tons of coal. If a third that energy had to be supplied from petroleum, it would translate to almost 260 billion barrels of oil per year. No matter how optimistic one may be about petroleum reserves, it is evident that some time around the end of the century the world's oil production will taper off and the gap in energy supply will have to be bridged by new sources of fuel.

Natural gas is not likely to be the fuel chosen to pinch-hit for oil; although it can be liquefied and handled in special tankers (see page 70), the process makes an expensive link in an energy-supply route. Because of the happy proximity of gas fields to energy markets so that they can be connected by overland pipelines, the United States has exploited natural gas as a national fuel. However, because U.S. gas supplies are limited, the supply curve must bend over sharply before the end of the century. What about the *world's* supply of natural gas? Much natural gas is found along with petroleum, and if reserves of the latter are 2 trillion barrels, then about a fifth as much energy in the form of gas or gas-liquids might be recovered. Obviously, this cannot take up much slack in the total energy supply.

The oil shales of the world do contain immense quantities of oil, but estimates of recoverability depend upon how economically the low-grade ores can be worked. But if the ore yields only a quarter barrel of oil per ton, then producing 10 billion barrels of oil per year would mean processing 50 billion tons of ore. The true extent of low-grade oil shales is an unknown quantity today and vast reserves must be anticipated, but the immense tonnages of ore that must be worked will impose an effective limit on exploiting this potential energy resource.

Returning to Figure 9-4, we see that our projection for the year 2000 can be fulfilled only if enough nuclear power is available to provide energy equivalent to about 6 billion tons of coal. This is consistent with the electric-energy year-2000 projection, assuming that, worldwide, about 50 percent of the electricity is generated by nuclear units. The rest will come from hydropower or fossil-fuel units, and the latter will presumably be less numerous after the year 2000 because of limited fuel availability. With the success of the power-breeder, the world's major nations will shift to a plutonium economy, and in the twenty-first century, nuclear-electric plants will become the dominant source of power.

Depletion of petroleum reserves will inevitably shift the energy scales to a coal-versus-uranium balance; and given the mining problems associated with solid fuels, nuclear energy will undoubtedly dominate the twenty-first century. With luck, fusion power may come into its own, lessening reliance on uranium and plutonium. But whether from fission or from fusion, the energy will be electric and will require the installation of very large plants at high cost. For this reason the rich nations will electrify their economies more extensively than underdeveloped countries; the poor nations will be hard put to find capital for building nuclear-electric units which, at the end of the century, may each cost up to $0.5 billion each (1972 dollars).

In Figure 9-6 one can see at a glance the distribution of

FIGURE 9-6

WORLD CONSUMPTION OF ENERGY
(1930–2000)
(By Continents)

Consumption of energy on a regional area basis obviously depends on import-export policies and on the degree to which nations will be able to form capital for deployment of energy systems. It is expected that on a worldwide basis, energy use will quadruple from 1970 to 2000. Less advanced nations may be expected to exceed this rate of energy utilization provided their economies can support the necessary growth. Asia's growth curve will be dependent on greater national use of premium fossil fuels. An extravagant export of petroleum would lower the Asian curve and enhance that of North America and also that of Europe.

FIGURE 9-6

WORLD CONSUMPTION OF ENERGY
(1930–2000)
(By Continents)

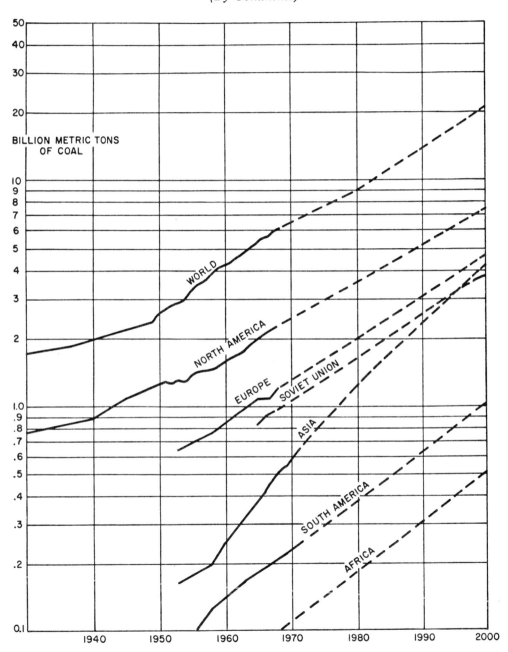

energy consumption. North America, Europe, and the U.S.S.R.—a limited sector of the temperate zone in the Northern Hemisphere—presently consume over 70 percent of the world's energy. The United States alone, with less than 6 percent of the planet's population, consumes 38 percent of its energy. Two great land masses, South America and Africa, burn up only about 5 percent of all fossil fuel consumed. The projections into the future show relatively little change in the energy status quo, except for an Asian surge attributable to Japan's economic resurgence and to the aggressive power program that may characterize the Chinese planned economy in the future.

A somewhat different view of how energy is distributed among various nations of the world appears in Figure 9-7. As the most electrically affluent nation in the world, Norway (13,570 kwh per capita in 1967) eclipses the United Arab Republic with its single kilowatt-hour per person. Norway, of course, is exclusively hydropowered due to its fortunate climatology and geography. More significant is the continental distribution of electric energy shown for Asia, Africa, the two Americas, and the world. The effect of continental averaging is to tilt the slanted line more toward the horizontal.

In a plot of total (rather than electric) energy consumption, the ranking of nations along the slanted line would change somewhat, with the United States standing at the top of the parade of points. The world's breakdown of energy sources is 40 percent liquid, 38 percent solid, and 20 percent gas fuels, with 2 percent accounted for by hydro-nuclear energy. Overall, each person on the planet demands the equivalent of about 2 tons of coal in energy production each year. But the extremes range from 22 pounds of coal equivalent per year for each person in Nepal to 14,000 pounds for each inhabitant of oil-rich Kuwait. Kuwait produces over 700,000 pounds of coal-equivalent per capita each year; a major exporter of fuel, it consumes less than 4 percent of its potential energy output, with most of that expended on its own energy industry.

232

With a little luck and good management, the energy-world will not end with the year 2000, and since the oil reserves constitute a one-time nonrenewable endowment, their too-rapid exploitation will deprive much of the twenty-first century of oil. The energy options available, especially to certain continents, are strictly limited. Some of them, like fusion, are still in their technological wombs, while others, like synthesis of oil and gas from solid ores, have physical and perhaps environmental limits. A modern Malthus with his eye on energy resources rather than people would surely see twenty-first-century man in serious trouble as he attempts to prosper, to move about on the planet, and to keep warm, in the life style of today's advanced countries.

First, let us consider the projection of U.S. energy consumption through to the end of the next century; then we will make the same estimate for the world.

Figure 9-8 is a graphical display of how such projections may be made for the United States. The upper curve assumes that in the next century the United States will follow a pattern of energy consumption continuing at an annual rate of slightly more than 3 percent increase. On this basis the United States would consume energy at the rate of 300 billion tons of coal equivalent in the first quarter-century and thereafter would slightly more than double that in the next twenty-five years. Total burnup for the twenty-first century would then add up to 4,750 billion tons, more than twenty times the energy consumed in the twentieth century. Clearly such an extrapolation is arithmetic absurdity and we need not dramatize the resource folly of such projection. It is more realistic to assume that the U.S. population will somehow be controlled so as not to surpass half a billion, preferably 400 million, by the year 2100 and that the per capita energy consumption in the twenty-first century will only double. Then the total burnup decreases to 1,500 billion tons of coal equivalent. This is the energy contained in 6,750 billion barrels of oil, three times the total world reserve.

Now let us make a similar estimate for the world, but this time stick to a single projection, since we cannot hope to be custodians of world population control.

Per capita consumption of energy has almost doubled during the past thirty years, and according to our projection (Fig. 9-6), it will reach a value of 3.2 metric tons per year by the year 2000. Let us make the assumption that there will be *no* increase in per capita consumption of energy throughout the next century—a rash one, since low-energy nations

FIGURE 9-7

GROSS DOMESTIC PRODUCT AND ELECTRIC-ENERGY CONSUMPTION

The per capita consumption of electric energy is roughly correlated with per capita gross domestic product.
On the log-log chart, the scale at the left shows per capita kwh; the one at the bottom the per capita GDP in dollars. Thus Norway, with its cheap hydropower, goes off the chart at the top in per capita energy consumption, and the United States is at the rightmost point in per capita GDP. The dollar gap represented stretches from Ethiopia's $63 per capita to America's $4,038, a factor of 64. The power gap is much wider: 13 kwh for Ethiopa to 6,614 kwh for the United States, a factor of 510. The relative positions of the points for four continents—Africa, Asia, South America, and North America—on both scales sum up the relationship of wealth to energy consumption.

FIGURE 9-7

GROSS DOMESTIC PRODUCT AND
ELECTRIC-ENERGY CONSUMPTION

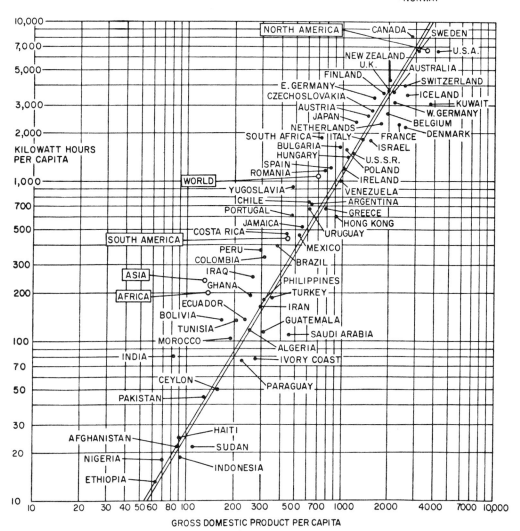

will be trying their best to shinny up the energy totem pole—
and further assume that the world population growth slows
down and follows this timetable:

Year	2000	2025	2050	2075	2100	unit
Population	6.5	8.5	11	15	19	billions

Even with our hypothetical energy freeze in effect, this would
mean a total consumption of energy in the twenty-first century equal to the burning of almost 4 trillion tons of coal, or

FIGURE 9-8

U.S. ENERGY CONSUMPTION (1960–2100)

The upper curve represents an extrapolation to the year
2100 of all U.S. energy consumption assuming that
growth continuously follows the pace of the most recent
decades. Such a slavish adherence to the ways of the
past being projected into the distant future yields
astronomic values for energy consumption—a total use
of almost 5 trillion tons of coal equivalent up to the
year 2100. This staggering total assumes continued
population increase and also escalation of the per capita
consumption of energy. The lower curve, a more realistic
but nonetheless impressive extrapolation, reflects only
a doubling of population in the twenty-first century and
rapidly saturating per capita consumption of energy.

FIGURE 9-8

U.S. ENERGY CONSUMPTION (1960–2100)

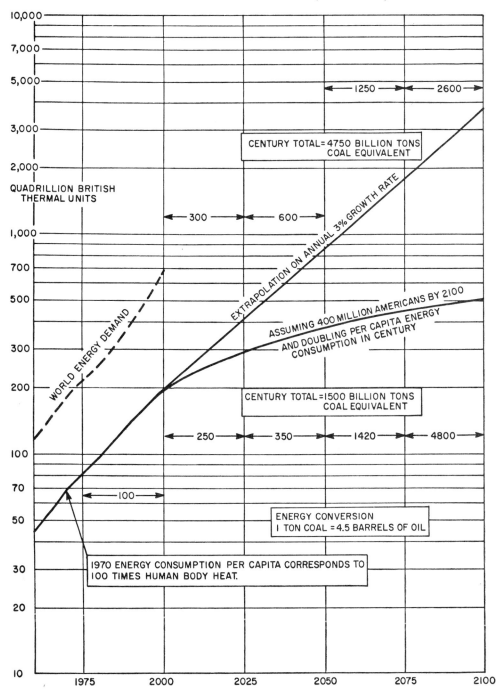

the energy equivalent of about 20 trillion barrels of petroleum. According to our estimates the supplies of liquid fuel will fall off during the first quarter of the next century, as will those of natural gas. The rapid depletion of premium fossil fuels, oil and gas, is explained not only by their great versatility as fuels, but by their relative ease of extraction from the earth and their ready transportability.

As a result of this huge exploitation, we will be forced to switch to the solid fuels (coal, lignite, and oil shales) for fossil energy and to heavy metals useful in fission. If the power-breeder is successful, nuclear power can potentially supply electric stations with the fuel necessary to keep them running throughout the twenty-first century. But even high-energy nations like the United States will find it costly to expand the electrification of their economies. Building electric plants is a highly capital-intensive business and, even in the developed nations, takes a very significant fraction of the total capital outlays. Referring back to the slanted line in Figure 9-7, we are looking at what is already a slippery slope for a poor nation to ascend; when only nuclear-electric options are available, the climb to energy affluence may be prohibitively expensive. Even the United States will find increasingly difficult the further electrification of its economy beyond the year 2000, when half its fuel use will be for electric energy generation. This is especially true if electric energy is to displace gasoline in transportation.

The record in Europe duplicates the U.S. experience in motor traffic nearly enough to make it clear that the pattern of individual or family mobility will infect other land masses as well (Fig. 9-9). However, the fuel requirements for European mobility will not compare with America's; the cars there are lower in horsepower and the cost of gasoline discourages the 11,000-mile-per-year use of passenger vehicles that Americans average.

The other continents hold a vast potential for motor traffic, and given highway systems and customer ability to buy cars, the people in India, China, Africa, and South America may become as car-crazy as the rest of the world. The growth rate of motor vehicles in Japan during the decade of the sixties illustrates how a new industry can take off in a foreign land. To be sure, most of the domestic vehicles in Japan are commercial, but the three-year doubling time for the growth curve is remarkable. The curve for Asia, boosted by the Japanese motor industry, is expected to exceed 40 million vehicles by 1980 and double again in the next twenty years. Any estimates of car sales in India and China must take into account the very low per capita income there, combined, in China, with a centrally planned economy. China, like the U.S.S.R., has tended to place priority on heavy machinery rather than on automobiles; this shows up clearly in the growth curve of motorcars for Soviet-Bloc countries. Both South America and Africa can be expected to offer good markets for cars, limited by the low per capita incomes of most countries in these two great land masses. Oceania—primarily Australia and New Zealand—is already rather rich in vehicles, and future growth may be expected to follow the U.S. pattern for 1970–2000.

All in all, the world by the year 2000 should have over half a billion propelled four-wheeled vehicles, or an average of one for every eight or nine people. The United States will lead in vehicular affluence, with fewer than two people per car, whereas in much of Asia there will be more than one hundred per vehicle. In India, and possibly in China as well, the development of a low-cost "jitney" may change these statistics, especially if governments authorize mass production of a standardized model free from Detroit's frills and annual style changes. I suspect that this will take the form of a four-wheeled motorcycle, powered by a low-octane-fueled Wankel-type engine, so it may be hard to take a census of "automobiles" later in the century.

If the automobile has been stressed repeatedly throughout this book, it is because the internal-combustion engine so vital to vehicular propulsion is playing such an impact role on the United States and other nations. Considering its

resource consumption, its pollution potential, its suburbaniz-
ing effect, and its weapons character, I think one is justified in
calling it the great self-destruct mechanism of the twentieth
century.

Although the internal-combustion engine is not the only
great consumer of petroleum products, it has been a demand-
driver and a prime factor in the ascent of the petroleum
consumption shown in Figure 9-5. The character of the U.S.
production curve which is going through its maximum will,
shortly after the turn of the century, be duplicated in the

FIGURE 9-9

MOTOR VEHICLE REGISTRATIONS
(Worldwide Data)

The similarity of the European and the American curves
representing growth in automobile ownership suggests
that the pattern may eventually be repeated in the rest of
the world. The precipitous climb of the Japanese curve
shows how a new industry can take off in a developed
country. Projections to the year 2000 put the North
American figure at almost 200 million vehicles and the
European figure at 120 million.

FIGURE 9-9

MOTOR VEHICLE REGISTRATIONS
(Worldwide Data)

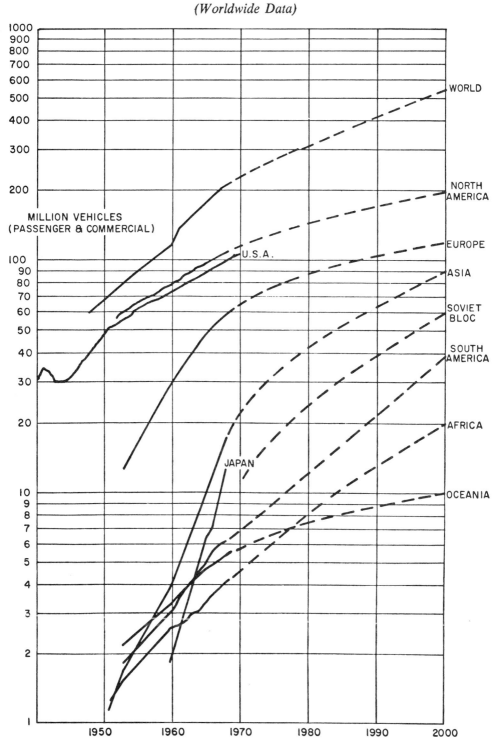

world production curve, so that it is no exaggeration to say that the world's supply of premium liquid fossil fuels will have been virtually exhausted within the span of not much more than a century.

In this respect the United States is the great exploiter of the fossil fuels. It burns 55 percent of the world's gasoline and uses 46 percent of the lubricating oil. It consumes 20 percent of the world's solid fuels and 63 percent of all natural gas.

The U.S. demands on nonfuel resources, such as nonferrous minerals, are increasing year by year, as shown in Table 9-2.

TABLE 9-2

U.S. CONSUMPTION OF CRITICAL MINERALS

Element	Annual Production 1968	2000		Cumulative Production Units (1968–2000)		
		Low	High	Low	High	
Aluminum	3,888	18,500–	36,800	290,000–	450,000	thousand tons
Arsenic	23,900	31,000–	52,000	895,000–1,103,000		tons
Beryllium	328	1,250–	1,740	22,000–	27,400	thousand lbs
Copper	1,540	4,900–	7,860	96,400–	128,200	thousand tons
Mercury	62,000	102,000–153,000		2,600,000–3,400,000		flasks *
Tin	59,000	71,000–	98,000	6,200,000–8,500,000		tons
Titanium **	441	960–	2,160	21,000–	33,800	thousand tons
Zinc	1,406	2,090–	4,000	57,000–	80,000	thousand tons
Zirconium**	63,500	110,000–220,000		2,688,000–3,952,000		tons

Source: Data from *Mineral Facts & Problems,* U.S. Bureau of Mines, Bulletin 650, pp. 432–33.
 * One flask equals 76 pounds.
** Nonmetal.

Although there are small deposits of tin in Alaska, the United States has no commercial tin-mining operations and is dependent on foreign supplies. Total world reserves are estimated to be 6.5 million tons—that is, only enough to supply the United States until the year 2000 at its minimum demand. The United States takes about a third of the world's tin, and new resources of tin or tin substitutes will have to be developed to replace it, as is being done by the packaging and canning industries, which are using aluminum and plastics.

Aluminum is quite abundant, with at least 10 billion tons in potential reserves of bauxite. The United States depends on Caribbean sources for 85 percent of its bauxite supply and uses over 40 percent of the world's aluminum. Aluminum's versatility will no doubt keep it in high demand. The result: even the 1.2 billion tons of aluminum contained in the known bauxite reserves will not meet world demand by the end of the century, when exploitation of new minerals will be necessary.

U.S. dependence on foreign sources for its raw materials is illustrated by Table 9-3 in terms of percentage imports (January 1971 figures).

TABLE 9-3

U.S. IMPORTS OF CRITICAL MATERIALS

Raw Material	Percent Imports
Tin	100
Industrial diamonds	100
Crude rubber	100
Chrome ore	99
Bauxite	99
Cobalt	95
Beryllium	93
Nickel	93
Asbestos	91
Manganese ore	91
Tantalum ore	85
Antimony	85
Fluorspar	77
Cadmium	70
Mercury	45
Zinc	40
Lead	37
Iron ore	35

The increasing consumption of natural resources reflected in Table 9-2 can be expanded to include rubber and plastics, which are in high demand. The United States has developed synthetics to satisfy most of the domestic demands for rubber. For example, in 1970 the new supply of rubber amounted to 3 million tons, of which 2.3 million tons were synthetic and 0.2 million tons were reclaimed rubber, leaving only 0.5 million tons of natural rubber to be imported. And the United States produced about 30 percent of the world's nearly 25 million tons of plastics and resins.

There is an almost endless array of statistics that may be used to indict the United States as the great consumptive economy of the world and the major depleter of the earth's resources. As we expand our horizons from the territorial borders of the United States to examine other countries struggling up the rungs of the industrial ladder, it becomes clear that they are following our example. Affluence American-style has become the goal of developing nations, and energy is the key to industrial riches. Hence the emphasis on energy on this book—especially electric energy, which will be the energy-driver of the earth's economy in the next century.

As other nations attempt to pattern their economies after this country's, they will be forced into the straitjacket of an electrified society for which their resources, both fuel and financial, are quite inadequate. The technology of the twenty-first century could thus condemn the poor nations to continuing poverty, and the gap between the rich and the poor countries will widen. This is hardly a blueprint for happiness on a planetary scale, and it singles out the United States as an island of affluence on a globe crowded with billions of people who will inevitably resent the contrast with their own standard of living. Through satellite communications and a probable global education-television hookup soon to be deployed, almost every village will become aware of the depths of its poverty and will sense the futility of hoping for human parity. Under the constraints of a sophisticated technoeconomy, an Indian villager watching a satellite telecast from America might just as well conclude that the picture originates on another planet.

One way to appreciate the impact of our logarithmic

growth is to project it for nations that will probably not match ours until after the year 2000, some probably not until long after that. Consider, for example, what quantities of energy would be consumed if every person on the planet now demanded the same amount of energy as the average U.S. citizen—that is, the equivalent of 14 tons of coal annually. This would mean a total consumption in 1972 of 54 billion tons of coal, if coal were the sole fuel; the actual 1972 consumption of energy worldwide was only 7.5 billion tons. Our comparison may not seem so startling unless it is related to the realities of the technology available to exploit fossil-fuel resources, but the differences between a high-technology country like the United States and the rest of the world become more apparent if we look at other items of consumption. If, instead of singling out total energy consumption, we focus on gasoline use, the comparison is more arresting. The average U.S. citizen burns 480 gallons of gasoline annually. If every person on the globe used as much, world consumption would equal 1.8 trillion gallons. And no doubt we would all be gasping for air on a planet perpetually smogged over with layers of motor fumes.

But long before other nations can equal U.S. consumption figures in certain sectors of their economy, planetary limits will prohibit such exploitation of resources. Petroleum shipments, for example, may have to be curtailed because of the pollution of the oceans resulting from tanker accidents. Obviously this is not the sole source of oceanic contamination; much petroleum pollution occurs as a result of offshore drilling and from inland dispersal of oil that ultimately finds its way to the oceans. But I fix on the tanker hazard as an example of the diseconomy of scale, the uncalculated detrimental effects of economy of scale that have invaded the technology of the twentieth century on the theory that "bigger is cheaper," which swells the size of everything from nuclear-power plants to oil tankers.

Oil first entered the world trade in the form of petroleum products, such as kerosene, for lamps and household use. At the time of the Civil War some 2 million gallons of this new fuel entered world commerce in sailing ships that took oil to sea. By 1907 there were twenty-eight vessels in the world's oil fleet, with a total of 142,000 dwt (deadweight tonnage, meaning transport capability). Before World War I the oil transporters were built with a 5,000 dwt capacity; this doubled after the war. In the early 1930s tankers with 15,000 dwt capability were built, and during World War II the famous T-2 tanker was born. The T-2 was of 16,765 dwt class, cruised at 14.5 knots and, operating 365 days a year, became the standard of the oil trade. A total of 525 T-2s were constructed during the war. In the 1950s the supertanker was born, out of the realization that larger hulls consumed proportionately less fuel for propulsion and also needed less crew. Tankers grew in capacity from 28,850 dwt to 85,500 dwt, and by 1962 the 100,000 dwt size became a reality. As the decade of the 1970s began, there were 3,185 tankers with more than 100,000 dwt capacity, totaling 140,-328,000 dwt. Moreover, there were soon 409 new tankers being built averaging 160,000 dwt each. The largest of these is over 1,100 feet long and has a draught of 81 feet; such craft are too huge for the world's ports and must be off-loaded by transfer of the oil to smaller vessels.

The increasing size of individual oil tankers is shown as the lowest curve in Figure 9-10; the curve second from the top displays the total capacity of the world's tankers, and the uppermost plot represents the annual deployment of petroleum in ocean traffic. Second from the bottom is the oil lost at sea as a result of accidents—collisions, fires at sea, and groundings or capsizings. (Lloyd's *Register of Shipping* for 1970 records ship losses at 352 for the year, and this fails to include groundings and accidents of the nonsinking type.) While prediction of future tanker losses is very uncertain, clearly the greater traffic and the total volume of oil at sea makes it highly probable that the ocean pollution due to oil contamination will continue to increase. True, I project a bending over of the topmost curve in Figure 9-10, and this might imply a similar behavior for the oil-loss curve. But the consequences of a single accident at sea are now immensely magnified by the huge capacity of a single tanker. In fact, shipbuilders speak of launching tankers in the half-million-ton class, and some even eye a million-ton capacity later in the century. Should such colossal tankers come into being, then a single accident at sea could equal the oil hazard of *all* the accidents that occurred in 1970.

When imports of foreign oil, especially from the Persian Gulf, shift to dependence on supertankers, as they will because of the sheer economics of the 15,000-mile sea route, the United States faces a double financial bind. We have already mentioned the balance-of-payments dilemma involved in purchase of the oil, but because shipping in U.S. bottoms is so expensive, the alternative of using foreign flag tankers further aggravates the trade deficit. In fact, in 1972 the Congress debated requiring the use of American tankers for 50 percent of oil imports, noting that otherwise the cumulative deficit for 1975–85 due to tanker carriage would amount to $14 billion. This estimate made no mention of the added cost of building offshore transfer facilities or deepening U.S. harbors to accommodate deeper draught vessels. Here is a case where the economy of scale in going to larger tankers rebounded to the detriment of a nation blessed with few deep harbors.

I think that we must speak in terms of the diseconomy of scale when contemplating the potential hazards associated with the *über alles* trend in certain technologies. The potential for disaster, it seems to me, argues for application of restraints on size, whether on the tonnage of tankers or on the capacity ratings of nuclear-power plants. Above all, we must not lurch into new technologies, opening up every door of opportunity, without careful examination of the possible consequences.

Many of the elements buried in the earth's crust are potentially harmful when introduced into our industrial complex. We have already cited the deleterious effects of mercury. American use of another heavy element, lead, amounts to about 1.5 million tons a year. About half of this total is used in the transportation sector, with lead storage batteries

accounting for half a million tons annually and lead in gasoline using up about half that much. Total U.S. reserves are
estimated at 50 million tons, with somewhat more than that
also being present in foreign countries. The U.S. Bureau of
Mines estimates that the 1970–2000 demand will total nearly
50 million tons, but admits that innovations in the transportation field could impose severe loads on the U.S. supply.
For example, if the electricar proves successful and popular,
it might require a quarter of a ton of batteries for each

FIGURE 9-10

OIL AT SEA

The lowest curve represents the growth in the size of
individual oil tankers. The curve next to the top
represents the growth in the total capacity of the world's
tankers. The increase in the tonnage of oil lost at sea
follows the other two curves with alarming regularity.
Supertankers of the *Universe Iran* class (327,000 ton,
175 feet in beam, and 81-foot draught) promise reduced
costs per ton-mile, and this becomes very significant for
long hauls from the Persian Gulf to the big oil consumers.
The shallowness of the Suez Canal prohibits passage
of even modest supertankers, forcing them to travel
14,000 miles to East Coast ports.

FIGURE 9-10

OIL AT SEA

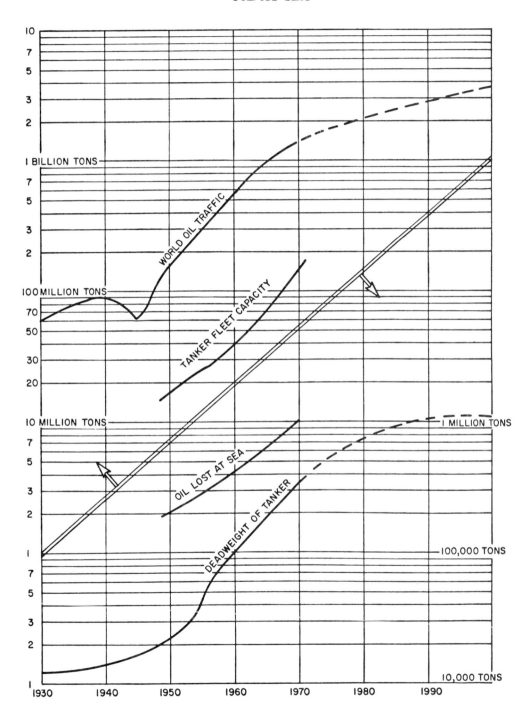

vehicle—more than a twentyfold increase in lead weight over that common for today's cars. Of course, lead cells would eliminate the need for leaded gasolines, but the trade-off would be a minor item in our national accounts.

But one cannot confine attention to a single resource when tinkering with a vehicular system that chalks up a total of over a trillion vehicle miles in a single year. Suppose that half of this traffic mileage were totaled by battery-energized vehicles, each of which averaged about 1 kilowatt-hour of electric energy expended per mile traveled. This would mean an annual consumption of 600 billion kwh for 1972. Overlooking transmission and charging losses, that would amount to one-third of the nation's annual production of electricity. To be more realistic we would have to move up our projection, say to 1990, when our electric-energy production is scheduled to exceed 5,000 billion kwh. Then the electricar demand would have to be adjusted for greater traffic at that time. Still, battery-powered vehicles would use up a fifth of all the nation's electric energy. Such an added load on the electric utilities would create severe problems for the nation's generation and distribution of power. Moreover, a power blackout for any length of time would leave uncharged cars motionless. (There will, of course, be countless mental blackouts when a car owner forgets to "charge it up.")

Such considerations, so often raised in this book, naturally lead to the question, Isn't the U.S. government anticipating these problems and planning to meet them? Two basic deficiencies cause such long-term issues to be shunted aside. First, at the top level, "political time" is quantized into time periods corresponding to elective office requirements; the result is that political leaders concentrate on fighting today's fires rather than worrying about tomorrow's. They are oriented toward thinking about problems as their constituents see them. Then, the government is not organized to tackle across-the-board issues of the type that surround the entire energy problem. In Congress there are perhaps twenty Senate and House committees and other groups each of which has one aspect of the energy problem under its custodianship. No single committee directs its attention to the overall energy issue; the Joint Committee on Atomic Energy specializes in nuclear development alone. Similarly, among the federal agencies, there is no single Department of Energy to reckon with the many phases of the problem. Instead, there are many separate agencies: the Department of Transportation, the Atomic Energy Commission, the Federal Power Commission, and the Department of the Interior, each of which overlords its own energy domain and resents interference or domination by others.

One is tempted, especially at the end of a book that has probed into some dimly lit areas of the U.S. and world resource exploitation, to break out in a rash of suggested solutions or "author emissions," but here that would be presumptuous. Given the complexity and the interrelatedness of energy to all the byways of modern society, I have chosen to concentrate on exposition and exploration of the issues, hoping to provoke public awareness of the grave crises that lurk below the horizon.

There is, however, a single emission I would like to make. It seems to me evident that as the United States goes overseas for more of its raw materials and as developing nations emulate U.S. industrial affluence, some global strategy of conservation has to be implemented. To this end I would recommend that a Global Authority on Resource Conservation be established to survey the planet's natural resources, particularly in the fossil-fuel sector, and to make forecasts of the allowable rate of depletion of these resources. In 1972 the United Nations convened an International Conference on the Human Environment in Stockholm, and it would seem just as urgent that it not just sponsor a conference, but act to establish an organization for monitoring the resources of the world. The United Nations already publishes annual surveys of energy and some other resource utilizations, but much more needs to be done to "get below the surface" and examine probable mineral resources that may be exploited. It is unlikely that the UN could tell an oil-rich nation like Saudi

Arabia to cut back its production for conservation reasons, but it could assess the rate of resource depletion and advertise the criticality of the petroleum problem.

Obviously the adjective *allowable* when applied to rate of depletion of a resource brings up front the key issue of value judgment. Apart from the problem of who makes these kingly decisions, there is the mind-boggling issue of the time dimension. We have concluded that the premium fossil fuels of this planet will be virtually exhausted after a century of burnup. Only a relatively few generations of man will be embraced by this era in human affairs, and while technology may be nimble and step in to energize future societies, we cannot be sure of this, nor can we be certain that the nuclear-electric era will bestow its energy bounty on mankind in an equitable manner. The pioneer spirit still infects the world and leaves future generations to shift for themselves. The least our present generation can do is to look where it is going and begin to think about the ethics of exploitation. Because the United States has been the fiercest industrial pioneer and the most all-consuming of nations, it is appropriate that it should take the initiative in global resource planning.

In a very real sense the logarithmic century is confined—both geographically and historically—to the United States in the twentieth century. The American soil and the climate of the 1900s have supported the luxuriant growth of an economy which exploited technology to limits that threatened further growth. The heady spirit of the pioneer prevailed and rocketed us to the moon, while the sheer momentum of the production line swamped the highways and the family rooms of America in a surfeit of goods. J. K. Galbraith's *The Affluent Society* (1958) took production to task and bemoaned the frivolity of elaborate automobiles, but it seems to have focused on the chassis and missed the gas tank. No word appears about resource depletion of petroleum and fossil fuels which were the key to U.S. affluence and which today add up to consumer fuel bills in excess of $100 billion. Few reckoned the costs or bothered to heed Nature's warnings that it could endure only so much insult and no more. And even fewer paid attention to the natural resources that consumer demands raided and depleted. When domestic supplies ran short, the United States imported and sought technological relief in the form of substitute materials. The logarithm of growth was disregarded.

The logarithmic growth which appears documented in the many illustrations of this book characterizes man's marvelous ability to wrest material from nature and fabricate things or, as in the case of fuels, to burn them up. Man's progress in coping with the problems erupting from this massive exploitation scarcely requires any logarithmic charting. In many respects the plot of man's ability to control himself and his environment resembles a plateau of stagnation. It is the rate of change represented by so many curves in this book that poses such a challenge to society. But is also the heady pioneer spirit of "full-speed ahead" that aggravates the issues of change. Thus the scientific and technological logarithms of change in this century stand in marked contrast to man's social inventions.

A penultimate word of explanation may be in order, for no mention has been made of the most serious side effect of growth associated with uncontrolled population expansion: I have steered clear of discussing the problem of human nutrition for the simple reason that there are already many books on the subject. A billion people are undernourished, and the lack of energy is a critical component of their anguish. Poor farmers in India manage to acquire water pumps only to curtail their use when electric rates are increased. But in a thousand more obscure ways energy is keyed to food production and, indeed, scientists like Dr. Alvin M. Weinberg, director of the AEC's Oak Ridge National Laboratory, have urged development of nuclear-power complexes to desalinate water in arid regions, provide power, and produce fertilizers. But such complexes come in the billion-dollar category and represent a high technology almost out of reach of backward countries. I would, however, add here that food resources constitute only one phase, albeit the most significant one, of what I would term *human parity*. A person born on the planet, it would seem to me, is entitled to a fair share of the earth's bounty—of food, of fuel, of all natural resources. Of course, this utopian state is far from being achieved, even in the most affluent countries, but human disparity seems certain to grow as the energy and resource quests of the major powers return only partial payment to the poorer nation from which the materials are extracted. When the oil wells of Iraq, Iran, and Saudi Arabia run dry, will these areas become the Appalachia of the world? It is true that foreign funds have flowed into the Red Sea nations, over $5 billion in the 1960s, but these were directed toward the goal of assuring a bountiful oil flow in return. Yet these nations have low per capita incomes, and the literacy rate ranges from 5 percent in Ethiopia (a compound of poverty and a 260-letter alphabet) to 15 percent in Saudi Arabia and 30 percent in the United Arab Republic. Some of these countries have more than a fair share of petroleum, but it is capital subject to constant depletion.

The affluence of the American island challenges the goal of human parity, for we have elevated ourselves to a standard of living, if not to a quality of life, that is all-consuming. We, the few, are poor models for the custodianship of the world's once-given store of natural resources. The logarithms of growth, which have been documented in this book, simply cannot be duplicated by the great masses of the earth's population. Indeed, even for the United States, the growth curves must depart from their vertiginous ascent—the twentieth century must, so to speak, begin to bend over.

Ours may well remain unique—the only logarithmic century ever to spin itself out upon a defenseless planet.

INDEX

Abandoned cars, 129–31
Abstract journals, 156–57
Abu Dhabi, 40
Advertising, 107, 112, 114
Advertising industry, 189–91
Aeroallergens, 14
Affluent Society, The (Galbraith), 252
Africa, 39, 223, 232, 239
Air transportation, 43–45
Aircraft horsepower, 51
Alaska, 35, 38, 40–42, 68
Aldrin, 126, 128, 129
Aluminum, 114–17, 242, 243
Aluminum oxide, 114
American Cancer Society, 190
American Nuclear Society, 203
American Tobacco Company, 18
Antigrowth sentiment, 136, 174
Anti-intellectualism, 135
Antiscience movement, 135, 204
Antitechnology, 151, 158, 160
Apollo (spacecraft), 50
Apollo Project, 144
Arkansas, 115
Arms race, 88–90, 149
Arctic, 40, 41
Asbestos, 13, 243
Asia, 219–23, 232
Atomic bomb, 85–89, 99, 140–41, 149, 204
Atomic energy
  peacetime uses of, 87, 90, 101
  secret research on, 85, 99

Atomic Energy Act, 92
Atomic Energy Commission (AEC), 21, 100, 176, 177, 251
  chairmen of, 41, 99
  creation of, 90
  credibility of, 200
  criticisms of, 92–93
  development of nuclear power and, 91, 103
  funding research and development, 142–45, 150
  powers of, 92
  publications of, 152, 154
  radiation standards of, 207–9
  spending of, 103, 142–45, 150
  statistics of, 101
  uranium miners not protected by, 196
Atomic Safety and Licensing Boards, 202
Australia, 239
Authority
  public trust in, 197, 198, 202
  of scientists in government, 198, 200–6, 210
Automobile industry, 23–30, 183, 184, 196–97
Automobile Show (1900), 24
Automobiles, 23–56
  abandoned, 129–31
  control of, 32, 34
  deaths from, 28, 31
  early acceptance of, 24–25

255

Automobiles (continued)
electric, 24, 250
emission regulation of, 25–26, 31–32
energy consumption of, 34–35, 43
gadgets for, 25
pollution and, 25–26, 31–32
production of, 24
registration of, 25
retail sales and services connected with, 184–85
steam-drive, 24, 30
worldwide, 238–41

Baccalaureates, 136–38
Bald eagles, 127
Basic research, definition of, 148
Bauxite, 114, 115, 243
Belgium, 22, 202
Bermuda, 34
Biological growth, 1, 7
Blaine, Henry H., 31
Bodega Marine Laboratory, 205
Boeing 747, 46
Bonsack, James, 16
Book of Prefaces (Mencken), 19
British Petroleum, 40
British thermal units (BTUs), 54–56, 180
Brown pelican, 126
Bureau of Mines, 98, 115
Bureau of Solid Waste Management, 132
Bureau of Standards, 139
Buses, 46

Cadillac (car), 46, 166, 171, 198
California, 63, 78, 92, 127, 205
California Institute of Technology, 82
Camels (cigarettes), 18
Canada, 22, 39
Carbon dioxide, 82
Carbon monoxide, 13, 31, 32
Caribbean, 115
Carnegie Institute, 85

Central Salt and Marine Chemicals Research Institute, 222
Cesium 137, 97, 129, 207
Chemical Abstracts (publication), 152
Chemical literature, 151–53, 157
"Chevy" (car), 24
Chicago, 68, 69
China, 219, 222, 232, 239
Chlorinated hydrocarbons, 126, 128
Chlorine, 14, 123, 205
Chrysanthemum cinerariaefolium, 123
Chrysler Corporation, 30
Cigarette advertising, 16, 18, 189
Cigarette production, 16–18
Cigarette smoking, 16–18
electric energy and, 80–81
negligence of U.S. government concerning, 15
reasons for, 18–19, 189
Coal, 57–59, 63
bituminous, 62
consumption of, 57–61, 66–67
gasification of, 58–59, 62, 69
GNP and, 12
liquefaction of, 58–59, 62, 224
miners of, 195–96
oil manufactured from, 42, 224
quality of life and, 12, 15
subbituminous, 62, 176
sulfur content of, 62
world supply of, 223, 224
College graduates, 136–38
I.Q.s of, 157–58
Commission on Population Growth and the American Future, 164
Compressed scale, explanation of, 4
Computers, 156, 157
Concorde (jet), 46
Congress, 25, 122, 172, 175, 200, 210, 250
funding research and development, 145–46, 148–51

Consolidated Edison, 190
Consumerism, 107–12, 114–23, 129–33
  natural resource demand of, 114–23, 132–33
  waste disposal and, 129–32
Consumption
  U.S., 107–14
  world, 213–54
Control of technology, 195–212
Contraception, 32, 34, 164
Copper sulfate, 123
Corporate interest, 23, 69
Council on Environmental Quality, 12, 14, 20, 82, 127–28, 175
Credo of growth, 1
Current Abstracts of Chemistry and Index Chemicus, 157

Datta, R. L., 222
David, Edward, 201
DDD, 128, 129
DDT, 123–26, 128
  accumulation of, 127
  banning of, 129, 200
  harmful effects of, 126–29
  malaria control with, 126, 128
Death statistics for automobiles, 28–29, 31
Defense science literature, 157
Dempster, Arthur J., 83–84, 86, 87
Department of Agriculture, 200
Department of Defense, 140, 144
Department of Health, Education, and Welfare, 31–32, 132
Department of the Interior, 20, 58, 59, 70–74, 251
Department of Transportation, 251
Desulfuring coal, 62
Detergents, 204–5
Deuterium (heavy hydrogen), 102, 103
Dieldrin, 127–29
Diesel train, 46
Docking, Robert, 202

Doctorates
  possesors of, 139, 158
  production of, 136–38
  as tangible manifestation of knowledge, 138
Dominican Republic, 115
"Doubling time," 7
Dow Chemical Company, 178
Drugs, 203–4

Eagles, bald, 127
Eco-economics, definition of, 22
Ecology, definition of, 22
Economic growth, research and development funding and, 140, 142, 144, 146–48, 150
Economic-political power, 20, 21, 30, 50–51, 132, 189
Economy, definition of, 22
Edison, Thomas A., 75, 139
Education, 136–39, 157–58
Einstein, Albert, 149
Eisenhower, Dwight D., 23, 140
Electric energy, 55, 74–81, 92
  consumption of, 7–10, 74–81, 107–14, 179–82, 220–23, 229, 234–35
  history of, 75
  motor vehicles run by, 24, 250
  wastefulness of, 72, 74, 79
Electric plants, 51
Electron-volts, definition of, 84
Elitism, 135
Emergency core-cooling systems (ECCS), 96
Energy
  definition of, 54
  importance of examination of, 22
Energy-intensive industry, 114–15
Environmental Protection Agency, 13, 14, 28, 123, 129, 133, 175, 200
  actions of, 176
  function of, 129, 195
  statistics of, 14
Environmental Quality Laboratory, 82

Erz Gebirge, Bohemia, 196
"Escape velocity," 50
Ethiopia, 234–35
Ethyl Corporation, 197
Eugene, Oregon, 174
Executive Order 11671, 201
Extrapolation, 80

Factories, 51
Federal Power Commission (FPC), 68, 78, 209, 251
Fermi, Enrico, 98
Fish, DDT in, 127
Fission, 84, 105
Floating Thermos jugs, 68
Food and Drug Administration, 200, 205
Ford, Henry, 24, 139
Ford Motor Company, 30
Four Corners (coal plant), 63, 176
France, 22
Freedom of Information Act (1967), 201
Frigidaires, 108
Frozen foods, 110–11
Fundamental research, definition of, 148
Fusion, 102–5, 150

Gadgets, 15, 25, 107–9
Galbraith, J. K., 252
Galileo, 135
Garfield, Eugene, 156, 157
Gas turbine engine, 28, 30
Gaseous-diffusion method, 86
Gasification of coal, 58–59, 69, 224
Gasoline
  BTUs of, 54
  consumption of, 186–87
  leaded, 172, 196–97
  profitability of, 172
  rationing of, 171
  sources of, 186, 188
  taxes on, 165–66
Gelbspan, Ross, 136
General Electric, 91

General Motors Corporation, 23, 30, 197
Germany, 84, 85, 146, 148
Grade school education, 138
Graphs, 4
"Greenhouse effect," 82
Greyhound bus, 47
Gross Domestic Product (GDP), 234–35
Gross National Product (GNP), 10–12
  coal and, 12
  electric energy and, 55
  measuring economic growth by, 12, 55
  percentage spent on productive research, 148
  quality of life and, 12
  relation of BTUs to, 55
  service trades and, 182
Growth
  concepts for description of, 7–15, 138
  indexes to economic, 8–12
  meaning of for affluent and non-affluent, 15
Haiti, 115
Hanford reactors, 90–91
Heat-electric hybrid engine, 28, 30, 34
Heavy water, 102, 103
Helium, 102, 103
Herbicides, 124–26
High Energy Physics Index (publication), 154
High energy physics, 149, 150
High energy physics literature, 154, 156
High school graduates, 138
  I.Q.s of, 157
Highway expenditures, 32–33
Hiroshima, Japan, 88
Hobson's choice, 47
Holland, 22
Home freezers, 110–11
Horsepower, 51–53, 198–99
  definition of, 54
  fuel usage and car, 25, 26

Horsepower (continued)
1970 average car, 25
per capita in U.S., 54
restrictions on car, 171
House of Representatives, 157
Human energy, 51
Hybrid engine (heat-electric), 28, 30, 34
Hydrocarbons, 13, 31, 43
Hydrocatalytic refineries, 188
Hydrogen, 102
Hydrogen bomb, 88–90
Hydrogen chloride, 14
Hydrogen sulfide, 13

Illinois, 92
Indexing of scientific information, 156–57
India, 126, 220, 222, 239, 244, 253
Indiana, 69
"Information implosion," 156
Information science, 156
Institute for Scientific Information (ISI), 156, 157
Intelligence quotas, 157–58
Intercontinental ballistic missiles, 144
Internal-combustion engine, 239, 240
alternatives to, 24, 28, 30
control of, 28, 30
pros and cons of, 30–31
International Conference on the Human Environment, 251
Interstate highways, 46
Ions, definition of, 103
Iran, 39, 40, 222, 254
Iraq, 40, 222, 254
Iron, 115–20, 243
"Isotopic Constitution of Uranium," (Dempster), 83
Italy, 22, 123, 126

Jamaica, 115
Japan, 123, 146, 148, 207, 219, 239
bombing of, 88–89, 204

Japan (continued)
energy and, 68, 165, 202, 219–21, 232
Jet fuel, 186–88
Jets, 46
Joachimsthal uranium mines, 196
Joint Committee on Atomic Energy, 251
Journal of Applied Physics (publication), 85

Kennedy, Edwin L., 179
Kennedy, John F., 140
Kettering, Charles, 139
Knowledge, 135, 136, 138
Kuwait, 40, 232

Labor force, 138
Ladies' Home Journal (publication), 189
Lapp, Christopher, 2–3
Lapp family, 24, 58, 179–81
Le Corbusier (architect), 15
Lead, 13, 123, 243, 247, 248, 250
Lehman Brothers, 179
Linear plot, explanation of, 4
Liquefaction of coal, 58–59
Liquefied natural gas (LNG), 68–69
Liquid Metal Fast Breeder Reactor (LMFBR), 100–1
List, E. J., 82
Lithium, 103, 104
Logarithmic scale, explanation of, 4
Los Angeles, California, 47, 82
Louisiana, 69
Lyons, Kansas, 202

Mackerel, 127
Madison Square Garden Auto Show, 24
Magazine advertising, 189–91
Making of a Counter Culture, The (Roszak), 20–21
Malaria, 124–26, 128
Malthus, Thomas, 213, 233
Marathon Oil, 68

Mass-transportation systems, 46, 171
Master's degrees, 139
Mazda (automobile), 30
Megaton, definition of, 88
Megawatt, definition of, 74
Mencken, H. L., 19
Merchant fleet, 51
Mercury, 13, 122–23, 129, 242, 243
Mesabi range, 115–16, 118
"Metallurgical Laboratory," 99
Metroliner railroad system, 46
Metropolitan areas, 170, 171
Middle East, 39, 40, 166
Minerals, 242
Mines' horsepower, 51
Model T Ford, 24
Monsanto Chemical Company, 205
Morton, Rogers C. B., 74
Motor vehicles, 23–56, 240–41

Nagasaki, Japan, 88
National Academy of Sciences, 200, 222
National Aeronautics and Space Administration (NASA), 140, 142–44
National Economics Research Associates, Inc., 181
National Energy Forum, (1971) 179
National Environmental Policy Act (NEPA), 19, 20, 133, 175, 210
  section 102, 20, 175, 210
National Science Foundation, 148, 149, 200
Natural gas, 54–55, 63–68, 228–29
Nature (publication), 83
Navy (U.S.), 91, 102
Nepal, 126, 232
Neutrons, definition of, 86
New Jersey, 92
New Jersey Central Power and Light Company, 91

New Priesthood, The (Lapp), 210
New York, 46, 47, 92, 129–31
New York Times, The, 166–67
New Zealand, 239
Newman, John Henry, Cardinal, 1
Newspaper advertising, 190–91
Nickel, 13, 243
Nitrogen oxides, 13, 28
Nixon, Richard M., 26, 59, 201, 210
Nobel Prize, 99
Nonprofit institutions, 146–47
North Africa, 39
North Carolina, 92
North Slope, Alaska, 20
Norway, 232, 234–35
"Nuclear burning," 84
Nuclear literature, 152, 154, 155
Nuclear power, 66–67, 83–105, 223, 229–30
  cost of, 84–85, 91, 92, 238
  development of, 90–92, 105
  disadvantage of, 102
  theory of, 83–84, 87
Nuclear power plants, 92, 93, 96, 105
Nuclear reactors
  commercial, 91–92, 99, 101
  containment systems of, 96–97
  cooling process in, 87, 94, 96, 97, 100
  core of, 93–94, 96, 100
  fuel cost of, 97–98
  Hanford, 90–91
  power-breeder type, 98–101
  pressurized water (PWRs), 96
  safety problems of, 93, 96, 97, 100, 102, 104, 105, 176, 177, 203
  water, 91, 97, 101, 176–77
Nuclear Science Abstracts (publication), 152

Oak Ridge National Laboratory, 253
Ocean liners, 46
Office of Education, 138

Office of Emergency Planning (OEP), 174, 175
Office of Fuels and Energy, 39
Office of Science and Technology, 200
Office of Technological Assessment, 210
Oil
  alternatives to, 41–42, 166
  conservation of, 167
  consumption of, 35–42, 66–67, 165, 167, 186–88, 240
  importation of, 39–42, 166
  production of, 35–41
  products from, 172
  reserves of, 35–39, 41, 42
  at sea, 41, 42, 248–49
  world supply and demand of, 226–28
Oil Companies of America, 166
Oil industry, 35–42, 167
Oil shale, 42, 59, 60, 62, 229
Oil tankers, 245–47
Oldsmobile, 24
Oppenheimer, J. Robert, 135
Organization of Petroleum Exporting Countries (OPEC), 40, 42
Oyster Creek plant (nuclear), 91

Pelican (brown), 127
Pennsylvania, 92
Pepsi-Cola, 132
Peregrine falcon, 205
Perl, Martin L., 200, 201
Pesticides, 14, 123–29, 200
Pesticides and Their Relationship to Environmental Health task force, 128–29
Pharmaceutical safety procedures, 203–4
Phillips Petroleum, 68
Pierce-Arrow Motor Car Company, 24
Piston plane, 46
Plasma, definition of, 103
Plastics, 243–44
Plutonium, 97, 99, 100

Political-economic power, 20, 21, 30, 50–51, 132, 189
Pollution, 13, 14, 31, 43, 175, 176
  air, 13, 14, 25–26, 120, 132
  thermal, 120, 122, 175
  water, 120, 122, 204–5
Polychlorinated biphenyls (PCBs), 205
Population, 1–2, 7, 162
  distribution of, 168–71
  energy and, 74, 79–81, 164–65, 167, 168, 171
  presentation of data on, 4–7
  U.S., 1–2, 7, 161–63
  world, 213–17
Possessions, 14–15
Power
  definition of, 54
  economic-political, 20, 21, 30, 50–51
Power-breeder nuclear reactors, 98–101
Presentation of data, 4
President's Science Advisory Committee (PSAC), 200
Pressurized water reactors (PWRs), 96
Price, Derek J. de Solla, 156, 204
Project Apollo, 144
Proximity fuses, 140–41
Public interest, 23, 69
Pyrethrum, 124

Qatar, 40
QBTU units, definition of, 60
Quality of life, 12, 31

Radar, 140–41
Radiation Council, 209
Radioactive Waste Repository, 202
Radioactivity, 90, 96–97, 102, 105, 207–9
  discovery of, 196
  waste materials and, 202
Radios, 108–10
Railroads, 51

Rankine cycle engine, 28
Rationing of electricity, 179
Recycling, 132
Red squill, 123
Refrigerators, 108–11
Register of Shipping (Lloyd), 246
Research and development
    funding, 139–51
Rickover, H. G., 43, 91, 101
Risebrough, Robert, 205
Roberts, Richard B., 85
Rodenticides, 124–25
Roosevelt, Franklin Delano, 85
Roszak, Theodore, 20–21
Royal Dutch (oil company), 40
Rubber, 243, 244
Ruckelshaus, William D., 28

Salt mines, 97
Saturation point of consumer
    market, 107, 108
Saturn-V (rocket), 50, 51
Saudi Arabia, 39, 40, 251–52, 254
Save-a-Watt campaign, 190
Schlesinger, James R., 41
Schmandt, Jurgen, 23–24
Science (publication), 19, 23, 200
Science Citation Index
    (publication), 157
Scientific journals, 151–59
Scientific specialization, 156
"Scientist-citizen," 201
Scientific authority in government,
    198, 200–6, 210
Seattle, Washington, 42
Seaborg, Glenn T., 99, 100, 223
Secrecy, 85, 99
Section 102, 20, 175, 210
Semilogarithmic graph paper,
    explanation of, 4
Senate Commerce Committee, 205
747 (Boeing), 46
Skelly Wright decision (1971),
    177
Sodium, 100
South America, 115, 223, 232,
    239

Soviet Union, 69, 88, 90, 149,
    220–21, 223
Space race, 149
Space shuttle program, 50–51
Specialization, 156
Speed, 48–50
Statistical Abstract for (1971), 55
Standard Oil of New Jersey, 40,
    197
State highway expenditures, 32–33
Stelzer, Irwin M., 181
"Straight line" projections, 2–3
Strontium 90, 90, 97, 129, 207
Sulfur oxides, 13, 62, 80, 209
Supersonic transport (SST), 47
Synthetic oil, 225
Sweden, 68, 206
Swordfish ban, 123

Tar sands, 42
Technocracy, 21
Technological ignorance, 145
Technopolitics, 20–21, 50–51, 145
Technology control, 195–212
Television advertising, 189–91
Television sets, 112, 113
Tennessee, 98
Tennessee Valley Authority
    (TVA), 63
Texaco (oil company), 40, 197
Texas, 40, 69
Thermal effect, 82
Tin, 242, 243
Tobacco Institute, 18
"Tobacco-agricultural-industrial
    complex," 18
Tracked Air Cushion Vehicle
    (TACV), 173
Trans-Alaska Pipeline System
    (TAPS), 20, 41
Transportation systems, 46,
    171–73
Trinidad, 69
Tritium (extraheavy hydrogen),
    102–5
2,4-D, 126
2,4,5-T, 126, 129

United Arab Republic, 232, 254
United Nations, 251
U.S. Commission on Population Growth and the American Future, 164
Universe Iran (oil tanker), 248
Universities, 146–49
University of California, 205
University of Chicago, 83, 86–87, 99, 148–49
Uranium, 74, 83–86, 97, 98, 196
Uranium dioxide, 93
Uranium miners, 196
Uranium oxide, 98, 99
Uranium-235, 83, 84, 86, 93, 97
Uranium-238, 83, 84, 86, 100
"Uranium and Atomic Power" (Roberts), 85
Use of Pesticides (report), 200

V-8 engine, 25, 30
Valdez, Alaska, 20, 41
Vietnam, 126, 140, 222
Virginia Electric and Power Company, 179, 180
Volkswagens, 46, 166, 183

Wankel engine, 30, 239
Washington Gas Light Company, 180
Waste disposal, 97, 129–32

Water power, 66–67, 232
Water Quality Improvement Act, 175
Water use, 120–22, 175
Watt, James, 54
Weapon power, 88–90
Weinberg, Alvin M., 19, 253
Western Energy and Supply Transmission Associates (WEST), 62
Westinghouse, George, 75
Wilson, Charles E., 23
Wood, 60–61
Work, definition of, 54
Work animals' energy, 51
World Health Organization, 123, 128
World War I, 24
World War II, 123, 139

Yale University, 138

Zero growth of electric power, 181–82
relative meaning for affluent and non-affluent, 15, 181
Zero population growth, 164
Zinc, 13, 242, 243
Zircaloy, 91, 93, 96
Zirconium, 91, 242